BEAT THE DEALER

A Scientific Analysis of the

World-Wide Game Known Variously

as Blackjack, Twenty-One,

Vingt-et-un, Pontoon, or Van John

Beat the Dealer:

A WINNING STRATEGY FOR THE GAME OF TWENTY-ONE

Edward O. Thorp, *Ph.D.*

RANDOM HOUSE NEW YORK

Fifth Printing

 Published in New York, New York by Random House, Inc. and in Toronto, Canada, by Random House of Canada, Limited.

Library of Congress Catalog Card Number: 62-19094

Manufactured in the United States of America

This book is dedicated to
my wife VIVIAN
and my daughters,
RAUN *and* KAREN.

Acknowledgments

I am indebted to Roger R. Baldwin, Wilbur E. Cantey, Herbert Maisel, and James P. McDermott for making available the computational details of their work on blackjack and to the M.I.T. Computation Center for making available an IBM 704 computer.

I wish to thank the many friends and colleagues who have made valuable suggestions, particularly Professors Claude E. Shannon, Berthold Schweizer, Abe Sklar, and Elbert Walker. I am indebted to Vivian and James Thorp for the long hours they spent playing the part of "the house." Also, for showing me many of the methods and devices used by casinos in cheating and for giving me a large amount of general information on the world of gambling, I owe a great deal to Michael MacDougall, special investigator for the Nevada Gaming Control Board, to some of the old-time Nevada "count" players, and to a certain crooked Nevada card mechanic. Conversations with a certain Federal investigator have given me a large amount of information about the inside activities and the out-of-state connections of certain Nevada casinos. Last, but not least, I wish to thank the two millionaires who financed the highly successful casino test of my system that is reported in Chapter 6. The Table of Random Digits, Appendix A, appears through the courtesy of the Rand Corporation and the McGraw-Hill Book Company, Inc., and is reprinted by permission from *The Compleat Strategyst* by J. D. Williams. The quotation in Chapter 7 from *Cardano, The Gambling Scholar,* by Øystein Ore, appears through the courtesy of the Princeton University Press.

There is a tide in the affairs of men, which, taken at the flood, leads on to fortune. . . ."

—SHAKESPEARE (*Julius Caesar*)

Contents

BEAT THE DEALER

1

Introduction

The game of blackjack, or Twenty-One, is one of the world's most widely played casino gambling games. For example, in the United States it is played in the State of Nevada, off and on in the city of Newport, Kentucky, and in numerous private clubs throughout the country. It also can be played in Montreal, Canada; Puerto Rico, Aruba, and other spots in the Caribbean; throughout the south of France; in the casino at Venice; and in other places throughout the world. In England, blackjack is known as "Van John" and in Australia, as "Pontoon." Both of these are corruptions of the French term *"Vingt-et-un."* In Germany it is called *Ein-und-Zwanzig* or *Achtzehn-und-Drei.* Although the name varies, the game is essentially the same.

In the modern casino game of blackjack, the player can gain a consistent advantage over the house by using the strategy that is presented in this book. This strategy, based on the mathematical theory of probability, was worked out by the author with an electronic computer. It is fortunate and perhaps surprising that the system reduces to a few simple charts which can be understood and memorized by the average player. In addition, the system lends itself to the rapid play usually encountered in casinos.

The rules of blackjack vary somewhat from casino to casino. A tabulation of these variations, based on my studies of many Nevada casinos and on questionnaires filled out by many of them, appears on page 157. A simple table shows the influence of these rules variations on the player's chances, and enables him to compare any two casinos and decide in which one to play.

No system can win when confronted with the chronic disease of the gambling games: cheating. Blackjack gives the dealer an excellent opportunity to cheat. Aside from not playing at all, the only sure protection seems to be to have the services of a card expert. But, by taking the precautions described in Chapter 7, the average player can protect himself sufficiently in most situations.

Eventually, when the strategy we outline becomes general practice, casinos may change the game or discontinue it. However, this will happen gradually, over a period of years, and even then, it will not take place in all of the many and diverse places where blackjack is played.

In the following pages we begin by outlining and discussing the rules of the game and then proceed step-by-step to advance the reader to any level of playing proficiency which he desires. The first step is to learn what we shall call the "basic strategy": a simple set of rules which tell the player when to draw or stand, when to double down, and when to split a pair. With the basic strategy the player's disadvantage, or average rate of loss, is less than 0.21 per cent in a typical casino—far less than the disadvantage in any other gambling game. Other published strategies for blackjack give the player disadvantages ranging from 2 to 5 per cent. The first substantially correct version of the basic strategy appeared in [2]. There were slight inaccuracies in this version and the exact version appears for the first time in Chapter 3. In casinos with favorable rules the basic strategy actually gives the player a slight edge over the house.

The basic strategy does not involve the counting of cards. However, after mastering the basic strategy, the reader will learn a simple modification, using a card-counting system, that identifies many situations in which he has an advantage over the casino of more than 3 per cent. Most people who are advised to count cards say, "But I can't keep track of all the cards in the deck. I can't even remember telephone numbers." They may be surprised to learn that they must keep track of only four cards—the Fives—and that this additional information, combined with minor strategy changes, is enough to give the player a comfortable 3-per cent edge!

The player who is willing and able to count more than four cards can go on to more sophisticated strategies, which are based on counting Tens or on counting Tens and Aces. On using the Ten-count or the Ace-Ten-count strategies, the player obtains an advantage which ranges from 4 to 15 per cent, depending on exact playing conditions.

Finally, for those who become experts, we present a strategy which involves only slightly more effort than counting Aces and Tens. By certain surprisingly simple devices, the player can take into account the effect on the game of every single card he sees. This allows him to identify nearly half of all situations as favorable to himself. In fact, half the time he has a slight edge as soon as he sees a single card!

For skeptics who do not believe a theory until they see it work, there is an account in Chapter 6 of a highly successful test that the author made in Nevada. Backed by $10,000, which was lent by two millionaires interested in making a profit, I purposely played very conservatively for about thirty hours. At the end of this time, the millionaires' $10,-000 had increased to over $20,000. As we became known, it became harder and harder to get the casinos to play a "nice" game. Some of the tactics casinos used included refusing to give us a private table, shuffling every hand or two, switching dealers in and out, changing decks constantly (one casino switched in four new decks in five minutes), and refusing to sell us large denomination chips. One casino even introduced a cheating dealer when we sat down to play.

Despite these annoyances, we were still able to get games whenever we wanted them. We finally quit because the millionaires had bigger business elsewhere, because my teaching duties required me to, and because the system had been sufficiently tested.

We think that this book will pay for itself many times over and for the time spent reading it. Anyone who frequents the gaming tables or who plays for stakes at home should be handsomely rewarded for his trouble. We hope also that some of the aura of superstition and mystery surrounding games of chance will be dispelled for the reader as we study blackjack together.

2

The Rules of Blackjack

The first step in learning the game of blackjack is to master the rules—with emphasis on the word master. Even knowing the exact meaning of the rules is not enough. The reader must be able to understand the effect of each rule and of each possible variation. Both experienced players and beginners should study this chapter.

Each casino has a set of blackjack rules which agree with those of other casinos on the main points but which usually differ in details. Later in this book we shall analyze the effects of these variations; but first for simplicity, we consider a typical set of rules. A set that is common, yet by no means universal, is listed below.

Number of Players

A blackjack game has a dealer and from one to seven players. We will see later that, generally speaking, the fewer the number of players at a table, the better it is for the player.

The Pack

One ordinary 52-card pack is generally used. However, some casinos use two and even four packs, shuffled together. It turns out that an increase in the number of packs hurts the player slightly.

The Deal

Before play begins, the cards are shuffled by the dealer and cut by a player. Next, a card is "burned" (placed face up on the bottom of the deck). The burned card may or may not be shown. The dealer then deals two cards to himself and to each of the players. Players get both cards face down. The dealer receives one card face up and one card face down. The two cards of the player and the "down" card of the dealer are called "hole cards."

Some casinos deal the player's hole cards face up. This is very convenient for players who count cards. On the other hand, seeing the player's cards in no way helps the dealer if, as is usually the case in casinos, he must act according to fixed rules. Later we shall see that about half the time a card is burned, the absence of this one card is enough to give the player a slight edge over the house.

Betting

The players place all bets except insurance (discussed subsequently) before any cards are dealt. The house establishes a minimum bet and a maximum bet. The minimum bet is usually between 25¢ and $5 and the maximum bet, between $100 and $500.

Our winning strategies involve varying the size of the player's bet. The player places larger bets in favorable situations; he places smaller bets in unfavorable situations.

The size of the minimum bet is of greatest interest to the player with a small amount of capital. The size of the maximum bet is of interest to the player with a large amount of capital because it limits the greatest possible rate at which he can win.

Numerical Value of the Cards

The player can choose either 1 or 11 as the value of an Ace. The numerical value of a face card is 10, and the numerical value of the other cards is simply their face value. We call a hand "soft" if it contains an Ace and that Ace can be counted as 11 without causing the total to exceed 21; we call all other hands "hard." Since there are two possible totals for a soft hand, we shall define the total for a soft hand as the number obtained by counting the Ace as 11.

The distinction between hard and soft hands is important. We shall see that the best strategy for a player with a soft hand of a certain total often differs sharply from his strategy with a hard hand of the same total.

Object of the Player

Each player tries to obtain a total that is greater than that of the dealer, but which does not exceed 21.

Naturals

If the first two cards dealt either to the player or to the dealer consist of an Ace and a ten-value card, they constitute what we shall call a "natural" or "blackjack." If a player has a natural and the dealer does not, the player receives 1.5 times his original bet from the dealer. If a player does not have a natural and the dealer does, the player loses his original bet. If both player and dealer have naturals, no money changes hands.

The Draw

The draw starts at the left of the dealer and proceeds in clockwise fashion. A player looks at his hole cards and may elect to "stand" (draw no additional cards); otherwise, he can request additional cards from the dealer, which are dealt face up, one at a time.

If the player "busts" (goes over 21), he immediately turns up his hole cards and pays his bet to the dealer. After each player has drawn his cards, the dealer turns up his hole card. If his total is 16 or less, he must draw a card and continue to draw cards until his total is 17 or more, at which point he must stand. If the dealer receives an Ace, and if counting it as 11 would bring his total to 17 or more without exceeding 21, then he must count the Ace as 11 and stand.

Many casinos alter this rule for soft hands so that the dealer draws on soft 17, or less, and stands on soft 18, or more; in this way they gain a small advantage. Some casinos gain still more by other variations of this type.

It is common practice for the player to request additional cards from the dealer either by saying "hit" or "hit me" or simply by scratching the felt table top with his cards. To refuse additional cards the player places his hole cards face down and may also say "stand" or put his cards under his bet. It is considered bad form for the player to touch the bet itself after the deal has begun. One reason for this is that players have been known to attempt, by sleight of hand, to alter their bet after seeing the dealer's up card.

The Settlement

If the player does not go over 21 and the dealer does, the player wins an amount equal to his original bet. If neither player nor dealer busts, the person with the higher total wins an amount equal to the original bet of the player.

If dealer and player have the same total, not exceeding 21, no money changes hands.

A player-dealer tie is called a "push." When there is a push, the dealer removes the player's cards without touching his bet. This often seems to be confusing so, to bring the "push" forcibly to the player's attention, dealers sometimes hold the player's cards face up and strike the table a couple of times before removing them.

If ties are a standoff, one might think that, except for the effect of naturals, the game is even if the player uses precisely the same strategy as the dealer. However, it has been observed that the player who uses the strategy of the dealer loses at an average rate of 5 to 6 per cent.* The reason for this is that if the player busts, he loses his bet to the dealer, even though the dealer may later bust also. Thus the case wherein both the player and dealer bust is an example of a "tie" that is won by the dealer.

* In *Scarne's Complete Guide to Gambling* [34] it is claimed on pages 19 and 317 that the book's author was the first person to calculate the bank's favorable percentage at blackjack. On page 317 it is also asserted that this percentage appears in the book for the first time anywhere. The bank's favorable percentage seems to mean (see pages 18, 19, 687) the average rate (i.e., percentage of the total amount bet) at which the player loses in the long run.

On page 326 of [34] it is remarked that it is not feasible to figure the exact percentage against individual players because their strategies differ widely. Also on page 326, full-deck composition is assumed for the analysis. Then on page 328 it is further assumed that the player follows the same rules (i.e., *strategy*, as the following sentences show) as the dealer. Thus the book seems in reality to be presenting the solution to the problem: If the player follows the same strategy as the dealer, i.e., stands on all totals of 17 or more, draws on all totals of 16 or less, and does not split pairs or double down, what is his average rate of loss?

To set the record straight we mention that Baldwin, Cantey, Maisel, and McDermott published the solution to this problem several years prior to the Scarne book, first in a mathematical paper [2, p. 439] and later in their book [3, p.27].

Splitting Pairs

If the player's hole cards are numerically identical, they are called a pair. He may choose to turn them face up and to treat them as the initial cards in two separate "twin" hands. This is known as "splitting a pair." The original bet goes on one of the split cards and an equal amount is bet on the other card. The player automatically receives a second card face down on each of the split cards. He then plays his twin hands, one at a time, as though they were ordinary hands, with the following exceptions. In the case of split Aces, the player receives only one card on each Ace. Further, if a face card or Ten falls on one of the split Aces, the hand is not counted as a natural but only as ordinary 21. Similarly, if a player splits a pair of face cards or Tens and then draws an Ace, it counts only as an ordinary 21. If a player splits a pair and receives a third card of the same value, he is not permitted to split again.

Doubling Down

After looking at his hole cards a player may elect to double his bet and draw one, and only one, more card. This strategy is known as "doubling down." A player who doubles down turns up his hole cards and receives his third card face down. A player who splits any pair except Aces may, after receiving an additional card on each of the split cards, double down on one or both of his twin hands.

Insurance

If the dealer's up card is an Ace, an additional wager is allowed before the draw. After checking his hole card, a player may put up an additional side bet equal to half his original bet. After the player has decided whether or not to do this, the dealer checks his hole card. If the dealer has a natural, the side bet wins twice its amount.

If the dealer does not have a natural, the side bet is lost and the play continues. The original bet is settled in the usual way, regardless of the side bet.

Suppose, for instance, that the player makes the side bet, and that the dealer has a natural and the player does not. The player then loses his original bet but wins the same amount back on the side bet, for no net loss or gain. This is why the side bet is referred to as "insurance."

There are a number of common variations on the rules for pair splitting, doubling down, and insurance. For instance, some casinos allow a player to split again if he receives a third card of the same value on one of his split cards. Variations such as this, which give the player greater choice, tend to increase his advantage.

Often the doubling down privilege is restricted to hole cards with certain totals. Variations such as this, which limit the privileges of the player, tend to increase the house advantage.

Customs and Practices

There are customs and practices connected with the game of blackjack which are not to be thought of as part of the rules. They vary erratically from casino to casino, sometimes in the same casino between shifts (casinos generally are open continuously, night and day, and there are therefore three shifts of employees), and sometimes even between dealers on the same shift. These customs and practices will have little bearing on the basic strategy of Chapter 3 but will be of interest in connection with the winning strategies to be discussed subsequently.

Shuffling. It is a custom that the player can request a shuffle at any time between hands. Similarly, the dealer can shuffle at any time *between* hands.

We shall refer to the practice of unnecessarily frequent shuffling by the dealer as "shuffle up."

Shills. A shill is a house employee who bets money and pretends to be a player in order to attract customers or to stimulate play. Shills may or may not be used in a given casino at a given time.

Shills generally follow "shill rules"; i.e., they never double down, split pairs, or insure, and they stand on hard totals of twelve or more. They often follow the dealer's rules for drawing or standing on soft totals. If the shill does not follow a fixed strategy he may be helping the dealer and/or house to cheat the players (see our later discussion of "anchor men").

New decks. The player by custom, but not necessarily by law, is supposed to be able to request a new deck whenever he wishes. Generally, new decks are first spread face down. Among other things, this gives the dealer a chance to check the backs of the cards for imperfections that in turn could be used by the player to identify cards that are face down. Then the cards are spread face up. This gives the player a chance to see that no cards have been removed from, or added to, the deck(s).

3

The Basic Strategy

During one Christmas vacation, my wife and I decided to relax from my teaching duties at the University of California at Los Angeles by spending a few days in Las Vegas. We both had been there before, but we were not gamblers. We enjoy the shows, the luxurious low-cost meals, and in season, the swimming pools.

Before we took the trip, Professor Sorgenfrey of U.C.L.A. told me of a recent article in one of the mathematics journals [2]. The article described a strategy for playing blackjack which assertedly limited the house to the tiny over-all edge of 0.62 per cent.* Because this figure is so nearly even, and so much better for the player than any of the other casino games, I wrote the strategy on a little card and carried it on our trip.

* Mr. Wilbert E. Cantey has told us that an error in arithmetic, discovered after [2] and [3] were published, shows that the figure given for the house advantage should have been —0.32 per cent, rather than —0.62 per cent.

When I arrived at the blackjack tables, I purchased ten silver dollars. I did not expect to win but wanted to see how long my stack would last, as well as to try out this strategy "under fire."

In a few moments the slowness of my play and the little card in my palm amused and attracted bystanders. The dealer could not conceal his scorn for one more "system" player. These sentiments were soon laced with pity when these people saw, further, the details of the way in which I played. Who had ever heard of splitting a pair of lowly Eights—and doubling the amount of money being risked—when the dealer's up card was the powerful Ace? Had anyone ever seen a player who doubled down on (*A,2*) against a Five or who chose to stand on a piteous twelve (hard) against a Four?

To add to this poor beginner's misery, the dealer was having a very strong run of luck. Every player at the table was losing heavily. Surely my ten "crumbs" would soon be swept away. Or would they? Somehow these weird plays kept turning out right. As other players lost heaps of chips, my little stack held. It even inched up once. After twenty minutes most of it was still there. Beginner's luck.

Then a strange thing happened. I was dealt (*A,2*). I drew a Two, and then a Three. I now had (*A,2,2,3*), a soft 18. The dealer had a Nine up, but he might not have had 19. Only a fool would draw again and risk the destruction of such a good hand. I consulted my card and drew. With no little satisfaction and several "tsk-tsk's," the amused onlookers saw me draw a Six. Hard 14! "Serves me right." I drew an Ace which gave me hard 15. Tough luck; I drew again. A Six! I now held (*A,2,2,3,6,A,6*) or 7-card twenty-one. This is an event so rare that it only happens once per several thousand hands.

After a moment of shock, some of the bystanders said I had a $25 bonus coming. The dealer said "No"—it was only paid at a few places in Reno. I was unaware of such a bonus. But I thought it might be amusing to create the impression that I had sacrificed my soft eighteen because I foresaw the 7-card twenty-one. "And who knows, they might even pay me." Of course they did not. But the amusement and patronizing attitude of some bystanders changed to respect, attentiveness, and even to goose pimples.

After another fifteen minutes—and after the obliteration by the dealer of all my fellow players—I was behind a total of eight and one-half silver dollars and decided to stop. But the atmosphere of ignorance and superstition that pervaded my little experience securely planted in my mind the suggestion that even "good" players did not know the fundamentals of this game. There might be a way to beat it.*

When I returned home, I began an intensive study of the game. I was convinced at once that a winning system could be devised with the help of a high-speed electronic calculator. As the first step in finding such a system, I used an IBM 704 computer to improve the strategy discussed in the above episode. It is this revised version—which I call the "basic strategy"—that you will learn in this chapter. It is the foundation for the winning strategies of later chapters. My calculations show that in a typical casino the house advantage against the basic strategy is a mere 0.21 per cent.† In some casinos the player actually has a narrow

* There will be numerous anecdotes and incidents concerning our strategies in actual play. They are here to make things "come alive." The reader is cautioned that one or a few incidents should not *in themselves* be construed as supporting evidence for the system.

† My studies show that the strategy devised by Baldwin *et al.* gives the house an edge of less than 0.25 per cent. However, the inaccuracies in their strategy are, for practical purposes, negligible.

Even though we used a high-speed computer for our analysis of blackjack, it was still necessary to introduce some approximations. The effect of those approximations has been to make all our figures for the house edge somewhat more pessimistic, from the point of view of the player, than the true figures. Consequently, whenever we say "the player's over-all advantage of 0.3 per cent. In casinos with the most adverse rules the player has a disadvantage of about 1 per cent.

Time and time again you will need to use this basic strategy while "waiting" for favorable betting situations to arise. It must be so completely memorized that any decision it calls for can be made without hesitation.

The Player's Decisions

As we saw in the last chapter, the game begins with certain preliminaries. When the players are seated, the deck is shuffled by the dealer and cut by a player, and the dealer burns a card. After the players have made their bets on the table in front of them, the dealer gives two cards to each player and to himself. As mentioned previously, one of the dealer's cards is up and the other is down.

At this point the player must make a number of decisions. The principal ones are whether to split a pair, if he has one; whether to double down or not; and whether to stand or draw. In general, what the player should do depends on the cards he holds, on the dealer's up card, and on any other cards the player might have seen. However, in this chapter the player completely ignores all cards he

---

advantage is 2 per cent," what we really mean is that the player's advantage is 2 per cent *plus* a small (unknown) correction factor which is *always to the player's advantage!*

For example, Dr. Allan Wilson has played over 300,000 hands of blackjack on a computer and his results show that the basic strategy gives the *player* an advantage of 0.16 per cent ± 0.07 per cent (sigma, the "standard deviation" of probability theory [9, p. 213], is about 0.10 per cent). Thus the correction figure to our figure of 0.21 per cent, for the casino advantage when using the basic strategy with typical rules, would be about $(0.21 + 0.16)$ or 0.37 per cent.

This difference occurs because in our calculations we have neglected, for simplicity, the effect, on the cards the dealer draws, of those cards the player draws to make his total. Roughly, this makes the deck "seem to have an excess of small cards"; as we shall see later, this makes the deck seem less favorable to the player than it really is. Thus our figures are pessimistic and the correction factor favors the player.

might have seen except his own cards and the dealer's up card. The basic strategy, given in this chapter, is a close approximation† to the *best possible* way to play under this assumption. Later, we shall improve our strategies by using the knowledge gained both from the player's seeing which cards were consumed on previous rounds of play and also from his seeing, on the current round of play, exposed cards other than his own and the dealer's up card.

The player's key decisions (pair splitting, doubling down, standing, or drawing) are illustrated in Figure 3.1.

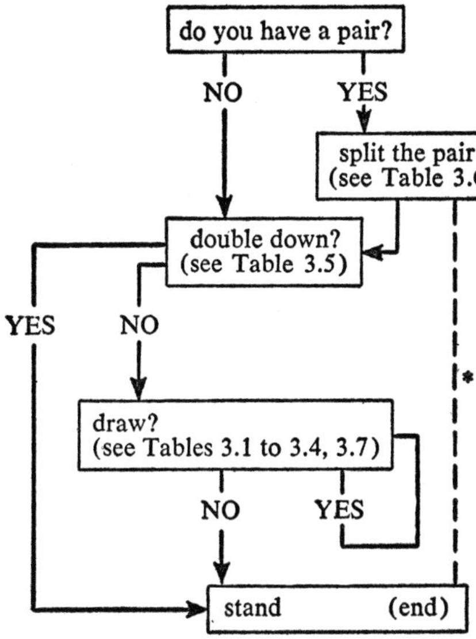

FIGURE 3.1. *The Player's Key Decisions.*

* Recall that when a pair of Aces are split, you are obliged to stand after being dealt one card on each Ace.

† A strategy that takes into consideration the specific cards which the player draws will on occasions lead to slight improvements. For example, on the average, the player should draw if he holds hard 16 when the dealer shows a *10;* however the decision between drawing and standing is close, with an average gain of 0.8 per cent in favor of drawing. By way of illustration, it is known that, holding (*10,4,2*), the player should stand when the dealer shows a *10,* while holding (*10,6*), he should draw!

The Basic Strategy for Drawing or Standing

In the great majority of hands the player will neither split a pair nor double down. Thus his decision is reduced to whether to draw or to stand. Since this decision is the simplest and most important part of the strategy, we shall learn it first, temporarily neglecting the possibilities of pair splitting and doubling down.

With a hard hand, consult Table 3.1 in order to decide whether to stand on your current total or whether to draw one or more additional cards in an effort to improve your hand.

TABLE 3.1 *Drawing or Standing with Hard Hands.*

Your total	Dealer shows 2	3	4	5	6	7	8	9	10	A
21										
20										
19										
18										
17										
16						draw	draw	draw	draw	draw
15						draw	draw	draw	draw	draw
14						draw	draw	draw	draw	draw
13						draw	draw	draw	draw	draw
12	draw	draw				draw	draw	draw	draw	draw
11 or less	draw	draw	draw	draw	draw	draw	draw	draw	draw	draw

☐ *stand* ▨ *draw*

To use Table 3.1, find the *column* corresponding to the card the dealer has showing and find the *row* labeled with your total. There is exactly one square in the intersection of this row and column. If that square is shaded, draw. If it is blank, stand. Figure 3.2 illustrates the use of Table 3.1.

Notice that Table 3.1 recommends drawing on all hard totals of 11 or less. This is reasonable because a player who does this cannot bust and must increase his total. There is one feature of Table 3.1 that is so striking (but not surpris-

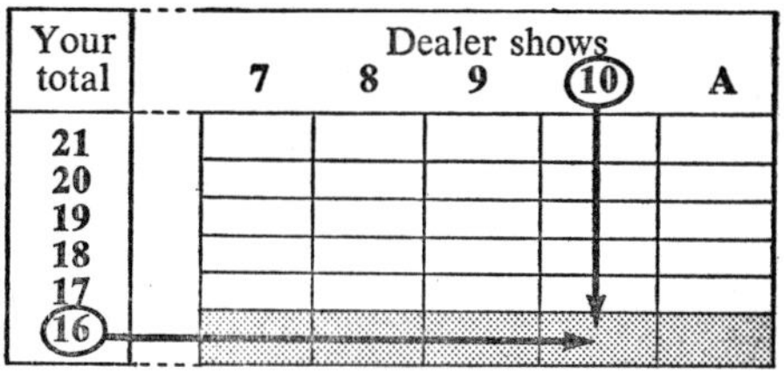

FIGURE 3.2. *When the Dealer Shows a* Ten *and Your Hard Total Is Sixteen, Draw.*

ing) that it attracts attention at once. If you should stand on a given total against a dealer's given up card, you should also stand on all higher totals against that up card. Similarly, if you draw on a given total against a given up card, you should also draw to all lower totals against that up card. This leads us to the concept of "minimum standing number (for hard hands)." When we want to keep in mind the fact that we are referring to hard hands, we shall say "hard minimum standing number." There is a hard minimum standing number for each up card of the dealer. It is defined as the smallest total on which the player should stand against the dealer's particular up card. Once we know the hard standing number for some up card, we know whether to stand or to draw: draw if our total is less than the standing number and stand if our total is greater than, or equal to, the standing number. Although the hard standing numbers can be found by inspecting Table 3.1, they are listed in Table 3.2.

TABLE 3.2. *Hard Minimum Standing Numbers.*

If dealer shows	2	3	4	5	6	7	8	9	10	A
Stand on reaching a hard total of	13	13	12	12	12	17	17	17	17	17

TABLE 3.3. *Drawing or Standing with Soft Hands.*

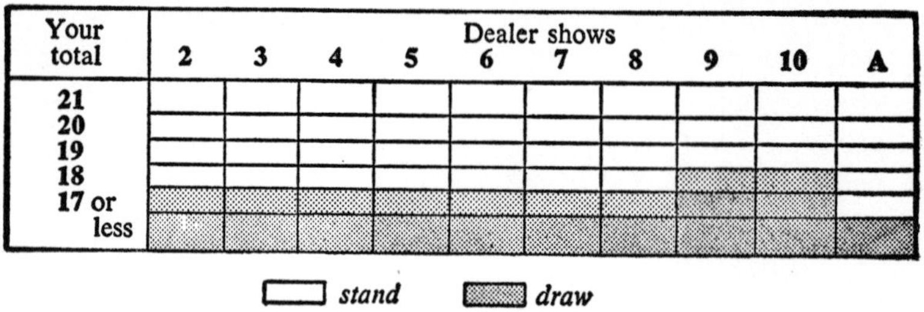

Your total
Dealer shows
2 3 4 5 6 7 8 9 10 A
21
20
19
18
17 or less
stand
draw

When your hand is soft, use Table 3.3 in order to decide whether to draw or whether to stand. Tables 3.1 and 3.3 are read in the same way. However, when we compare them, we see that drawing is recommended for much higher totals with soft hands than with hard hands. Part of the reason for this difference can be seen from the following argument. Remember we saw that a player with a hard total of 11 or less has nothing to lose by drawing one more card. Similarly, a player with a soft total of 16 or less has nothing to lose. Since his hand is soft, he cannot bust by drawing a card because if it puts him over 21 when he continues to count the Ace as 11, he automatically counts it as one instead. This reduction of ten in his total will keep the player from busting no matter which card was drawn. If an Ace was drawn, it can be counted as one, if necessary, and any other card will have a numerical value of ten or less.

Since the player with a soft total of 16 or less cannot bust by drawing one more card, he cannot make his total poorer. This is because all final, or "standing" totals of 16 or less are equivalent. If you stand and the dealer busts, you win the same amount no matter what your total is. Whether it is 16, or less than 16, makes no difference. If you stand on 16 or less and the dealer does not bust, then by the rules he must have ended up with a total between 17 and 21. Thus he automatically beats all totals of 16 and under. Therefore, if you draw to soft 16 or less, you cannot harm yourself. In fact, you may even be able to help yourself. For example, on holding (*A,5*), you improve your chances to tie or win if the card you draw is any one of the group *A,2,3,4,5;* on holding (*A,2,A*), you improve your chances to tie or win if the card you draw is any one of the group *3,4,5,6,7*.

When drawing to a soft 17, there is a small possibility of loss. If you stand and the dealer also has 17, you will tie him and thus avoid the loss of your bet. However, if you draw to soft 17, you may convert your hand into a hard hand that totals less than 17. If you then stand on this, you are worse off than before for the dealer may end up with exactly 17 and now you lose wherein you would have tied. If you draw to this hard hand, you may bust and lose at once. For example, with (*A,3,3*)=soft 17, suppose a Five is drawn to make (*A,3,3,5*)=hard 12. If the dealer shows a Five, Table 3.4 recommends standing. If the dealer shows an Ace, the table recommends drawing. If a *10* is drawn, we reach (*A,3,3,5,10*)=*22* (even counting the Ace as one) and bust.

Despite this chance of making your hand poorer by drawing to a soft 17, calculations show that this risk is more than offset by the possibilty of improving your hand. Thus, with (*A,6*), you may draw an *A,2,3,* or *4,* all of which improve your hand. Even if you draw a *5,6,7,8,9,* or *10,* you do not bust. You still have another draw, if you wish, with which to try for a good total.

It sometimes takes a little will power to follow these instructions. More than once I have been confronted with heart-stoppers like the following. I was playing a "big-money" game in a certain Nevada casino. By the card-counting methods of later chapters, I knew that I had a 5 per cent edge on the next round of play. Therefore, I had placed the maximum bet of $500. The dealer's up card was a *7*. I was dealt (*A,6*), a soft 17. Since the remaining cards in the deck consisted largely of Tens, I was fairly certain that the dealer had 17. Since there were only four cards that would help me—the *A,2,3,4*—and five that would hurt me—the *5,6,7,8,9*, I was reluctant to draw and was inclined to play for a tie. Nevertheless, I gritted my teeth and drew once, receiving an *8*. I now held hard 15. I held my breath and drew again; this time I received an Ace. I now held hard 16. Resignedly, I drew again, receiving—to my amazement—a *3*. I now decided to stand with my hard 19. When the dealer exposed his hand, to my surprise, he held what happened to be the only Ace yet unaccounted for (one had already appeared on an earlier round of play). According to the rules of the game he was required to stand. The basic strategy not only produced the only line of play that could save the $500, it even doubled the money.

We see from Table 3.3 that there are minimum standing numbers for drawing and standing with soft hands that are similar to those for drawing or standing with hard hands. Thus you should draw if your soft total is less than the soft standing number given for the current up card of the dealer, and stand if your soft total is greater than or equal to this standing number. Soft minimum standing numbers are listed in Table 3.4.

TABLE 3.4. *Soft Minimum Standing Numbers.*

If dealer shows	**2**	**3**	**4**	**5**	**6**	**7**	**8**	**9**	**10**	**A**
Stand on reaching a soft total of	**18**	**18**	**18**	**18**	**18**	**18**	**18**	**19**	**19**	**18**

The reader who practices with the basic strategy may or may not find that, in the beginning, Tables 3.1 and 3.3 are easier to use than Tables 3.2 and 3.4. He should use the ones he prefers. In either case, he will soon know the standing numbers well enough to dispense with all the Tables 3.1-3.4.

Basic Strategy for Doubling Down

The part of the strategy which is next in importance, as well as next in simplicity, is hard doubling down. For completeness, we shall discuss soft doubling down also. It is probably more convenient to postpone memorizing this until after pair splitting has been learned.

As indicated in Figure 3.1, the decision of whether or not to double down must be made before that of drawing versus standing. This decision is made by using Table 3.5. The possible up cards of the dealer are again listed in a row across the top of the table. The player's totals are again listed in the column on the left. In order to decide whether to double down, first see if your total appears in the column on the left. If it does not appear, you should not double down. Proceed to make the next decision, that is, whether to draw or stand. If your total does appear, run down the column below the dealer's up card until you reach the row that has your total appearing on the left. If the square at this location contains an S, double down only if your hand is soft. If the square contains an H, double down only if your hand is hard. If the square is blank, do not double down, but go to the next step, that of deciding whether to draw or stand.

To illustrate the use of Table 3.5, suppose that the dealer shows a *3* and you have been dealt (*A*,*6*), or soft 17. On locating the appropriate square, as illustrated in Figure 3.3, you find an S; therefore you double down.

There are several things to notice about Table 3.5. First, there are no squares containing both S and H. This means that there are no situations in which the player doubles down on the same total, regardless of whether it is hard or soft. Second, note that hard doubling down is done only on totals of 11 or less and soft doubling down is done only on totals of 13 or more.

In the table the row corresponding to a player's total of 12 has been omitted. This is because a player never doubles down on 12: with hard 12, the probability of busting is too large; soft 12 happens only with a pair of Aces and it is always much better to split the pair than to double down.

Observe that the player always (exception noted in table) doubles down on hard 11. With hard 10, the player doubles down except against an Ace or a Ten. Hard 10 is a less favorable total than hard 11, because the total the player obtains when doubling down on hard 10 is one less than the total that he would have obtained when doubling down on hard 11, except when an Ace is drawn. Hard 9 is even less favorable than hard 10, and with hard 8, the player does not double down at all.

TABLE 3.5. *Doubling Down.*

Your total	Dealer shows 2	3	4	5	6	7	8	9	10	A
18		S	S	S	S					
17		S	S	S	S					
16			S	S	S					
15			S	S	S					
14			S	S	S					
13				S	S					
11	H	H	H	H	H	H	H	H	H	H*
10	H	H	H	H	H	H	H	H		
9	H	H	H	H	H					

S — *double down on soft total only*
H — *double down on hard total only*
(blank) — *do not double down*

* The player should not double down but, rather, should draw on (9,2) = 11 if the dealer's up card is an Ace. However, the decision is so close that it can, for all practical purposes, be ignored.

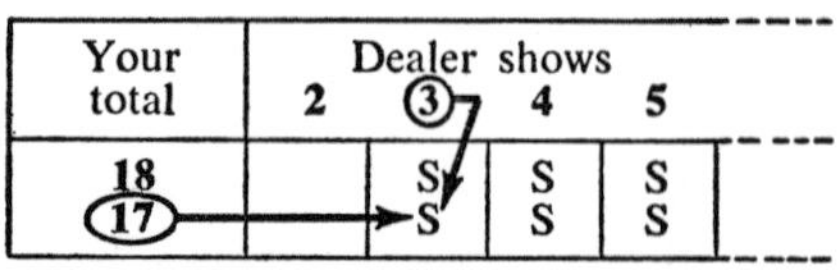

FIGURE 3.3. *When the Dealer's Up Card Is* Three, *and Your Total Is* Soft *Seventeen, Double Down.*

The pattern persists with soft doubling down also. The player doubles down on soft totals most frequently when holding the highest total for which doubling down is recommended. As the total drops, soft doubling down becomes less favorable. A conspicuous feature of the table is that soft doubling down is never recommended against *7,8,9,10,* or *A*. Later in the chapter, when we study all the strategy tables as a group, we shall see the reasons for this.

It is hard to explain the doubling down strategies without using mathematics. But experience in actual play soon engraves them on the memory. I always remember to double down on soft 13 against a Five because of a specific hand that arose once in Las Vegas. On this particular occasion, my friends and I had gone to one of the casinos to feel out the territory to see whether this particular casino would play on a larger scale without quitting as soon as we would begin to win substantial amounts. I was varying my bets from $1 to $10. Because I had frequently bet only $1, we agreed that I was not to raise my bets above $10—to do so would attract attention. However, a juicy situation arose (a 6 per cent advantage). I could not resist! I shoved out $30. To my satisfaction, the dealer's up card turned out to be a Five, the most favorable card for the player. Confidently, I turned up my (*A,2*) hole cards and doubled my bet. I did not bother to look at the down card that was dealt to me because I expected the dealer to have a Ten down and then to draw another card—busting himself. To my horror, the dealer's hole card was a Four. He drew the expected Ten for a total of 19. I was resigned to a loss when the dealer turned up my hole card to settle the bet. My hole card was a Seven!

There was a strange expression on the dealer's face. Luck by itself was one thing, but the abnormally large bet I made in advance smacked of prescience. I was almost "given away." What the dealer did not realize was that he was as lucky to have a Four underneath as I was to draw a Seven. One of the characteristics of the basic strategy is that, by using it, you will be considerably "luckier" than the average player. In this instance, my "luck" proved embarrassing.

Basic Strategy for Splitting Pairs

After memorizing the strategy for drawing and standing and for hard doubling (soft doubling too, if the rest is easy), you are ready to add pair splitting to your repertoire. The detailed pair-splitting strategy will be described, followed by a simple way to learn it.

If you have a pair, Figure 3.1 shows that the first decision you have to make, before either doubling down or drawing and standing, is whether or not to split it. You can decide this by using Table 3.6. In that table, the possible up cards of the dealer are listed in a row across the top and the possible pairs of the player are listed in the column on the left. If you have a pair, run down the column below the dealer's up card until you get to the row labeled with your pair. If the square at this location is blank, do not split your pair. Proceed immediately to Table 3.5. If, on the other hand, the square (in Table 3.6) is shaded, first split your pair and then go on to Table 3.5. If you have no pair, as is the case in about six times out of seven, skip Table 3.6 altogether; go directly to Table 3.5.

Figure 3.4 illustrates the use of Table 3.6. Suppose the dealer shows a *3* and you have a pair of *9*'s. Since the appropriate square in Figure 3.4 is shaded, the pair is split.

If Table 3.6 seems imposing, you may replace it by an *approximate* set of rules. They are: always split Aces and Eights; never split Fours, Fives, or Tens; split other cards when the dealer shows Two through Seven, and not otherwise. The heavy lines in Table 3.6 indicate *this* set of rules. Notice that the approximation introduces only five errors. Some of these errors are quite large but, because the situa-

TABLE 3.6. *Pair Splitting.*

Your pair	Dealer shows 2	3	4	5	6	7	8	9	10	A
A,A	split	split	split	split	split	split	split	split	split	split
10,10										
9,9	split	split	split	split	split		split	split		
8,8	split	split	split	split	split	split	split	split	split	split
7,7	split	split	split	split	split	split	split			
6,6	split	split	split	split	split	split				
5,5										
4,4				split						
3,3	split	split	split	split	split	split				
2,2	split	split	split	split	split	split				

(blank square) *do not split pair*
(shaded square) *split pair*

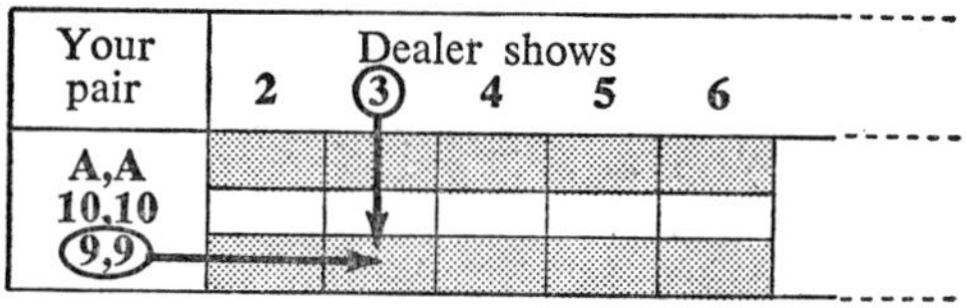

FIGURE 3.4. *When the Dealer's Up Card Is* Three, *Split a Pair of* Nines.

tions arise infrequently, the effect on the over-all house advantage is to give the house an additional 0.13 per cent. Once you have learned to use these approximate pair-splitting rules with your doubling-down and standing-versus-drawing strategy, you are ready to learn the pair-splitting strategy in detail.

The one hundred pieces of information in Table 3.6 are easier to learn by visualizing the arrangement of the squares. For example, the information in forty of the squares is contained in the rule, "Always split Aces and Eights, never split Fives and Tens." There are "reasons" for these rules that may help you to retain them.* Aces should be split

* These "reasons" are only a very crude picture of the actual state of affairs. The precise situation is given in Appendix B. We give "reasons" here to help you fix the rules in your mind without having to worry about involved mathematical points. Those who need further assistance might consult [12].

because there is a very good chance of getting a winning hand—even twenty-one—with each of the new hands, whereas the original hand (*A,A*) is only fair for doubling down or for drawing or standing.

If the dealer has a *7,8,9,10,* or *A* up, Eights should be split, not so much because a good total will be obtained with each new hand but rather because 16 is, in general, a bad total to hold. The reason that 16 is unfavorable is this. When the dealer's up card is Seven or higher, he is not likely to bust; and if he does not bust, he is sure to beat 16. Thus, the splitting of Eights against *7* through *A* "breaks up" a bad hand.

It turns out that the new hands are not very unfavorable (in fact, they have about an average chance of winning), and even though you are staking more money, your net loss is greatly reduced. When the dealer shows a *2,3,4,5,* or *6,* the splitting of Eights gains in two ways. First, a bad hand is replaced by two average ones. Secondly, the dealer's chance of busting is quite high with these up cards, and thus there is an advantage in getting more money onto the table.

The splitting of Tens is unfavorable because it generally replaces one very good hand (twenty) by two that are generally just a little better than average. Splitting Fives is not advantageous because it replaces a total that is good to double down on or good to draw to, by what are likely to be two poor hands.

Notice that the strategy is the same for Twos, Threes, and Sixes—split only if the dealer shows any card *2* through *7*.

The strategy for Sevens stuck in my mind simply because Sevens are split when the dealer shows any card *2* through *8*, and *8* is one more than *7*. With Nines, split when the dealer shows *2* through *9* (nine-9 should be easy to remember) with this exception: do not split Nines when the dealer shows a Seven. Here is a way of remembering that exception. Two Nines give a total of 18. If the dealer shows a Seven, a total of 17 is much more likely than usual for him (see Appendix B, Table 1, Dealer's Probabilities); it pays to stand on the hope of beating him.

In Table 3.7, we have combined the ideas of Tables 3.1 to 3.4.

TABLE 3.7. *Hard and Soft Standing Numbers.*

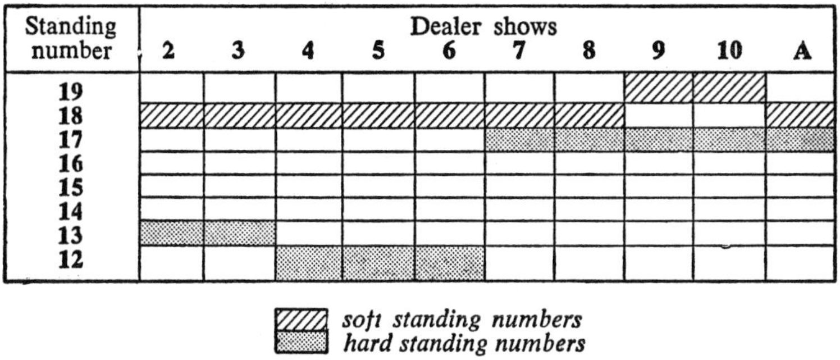

Standing number
Dealer shows
2 3 4 5 6 7 8 9 10 A
19
18
17
16
15
14
13
12
soft standing numbers
hard standing numbers

Table 3.7 is used somewhat differently than the previous tables. It is a table for looking up any standing number. For instance, in order to find your standing number, locate the dealer's up card in the row across the top. Run down the column below that up card until you come to one of two shaded boxes. The lightly shaded boxes are for soft hands; the darkly shaded boxes are for hard hands. The standing number appears to the left of the row the box is in. Figures 3.5 and 3.6 illustrate this procedure.

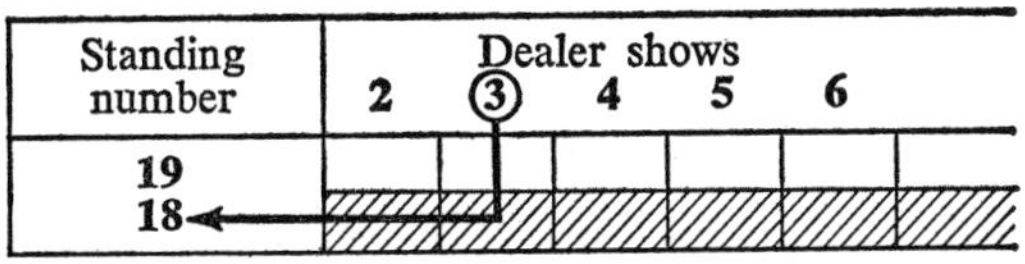

FIGURE 3.5. *When the Dealer's Up Card Is* Three, *the Player's* Soft *Minimum Standing Number Is Eighteen.*

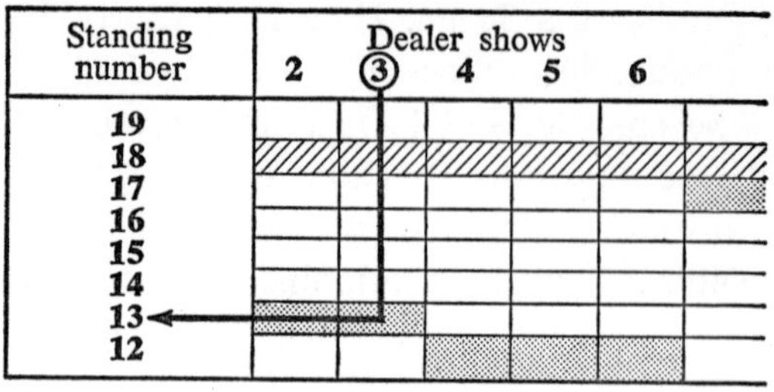

FIGURE 3.6. *When the Dealer's Up Card Is* Three, *the Player's* Hard *Minimum Standing Number Is Thirteen.*

The set of lightly shaded boxes in Table 3.7 is a kind of "picture" or graph of the information in Table 3.4. Similarly, the darkly shaded boxes are a picture or graph of Table 3.2. It may be helpful, when using Table 3.7, for you to think of the standing numbers as goals and that you must either reach or bust yourself in the attempt.

It may seem strange that we have gone to all this trouble to organize the material in Tables 3.1 and 3.3 into Tables 3.2 and 3.4, and this into Table 3.7. The reason is that Table 3.7 is the best compromise between simplicity (Tables 3.1 and 3.3) and compactness (Tables 3.2 and 3.4) that we have been able to find for our *future* needs. In succeeding chapters, the more refined and powerful strategies, will be organized into tables. It is desirable that these tables all have the same familiar, simple form. The format of Tables 3.5, 3.6, and 3.7 suits all needs. It is also desirable that these tables be compact in order that they can be readily used in miniature form in the casinos. The miniaturization and format of the standard strategy which appears in Table 3.8 is also typical of that of our winning strategies.

A copy of Table 3.8 appears at the end of the book in a pocket containing "detachable charts for casino reference." The card may be removed from the pocket and cupped inconspicuously in the palm while playing. As you become more expert you will consult the card less frequently and finally not at all.

TABLE 3.8. *A Complete Miniature Version of the Basic Strategy.*

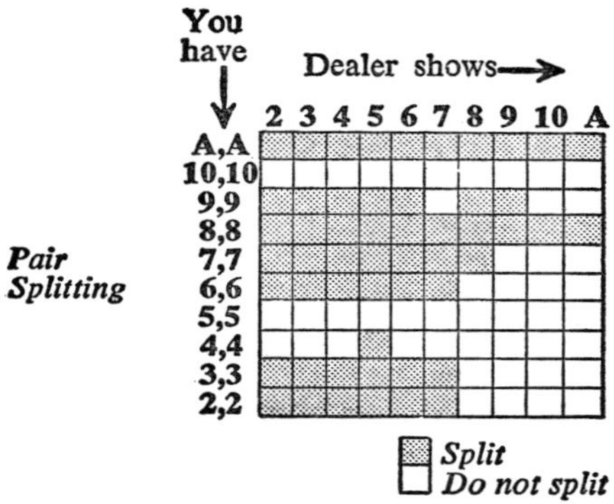

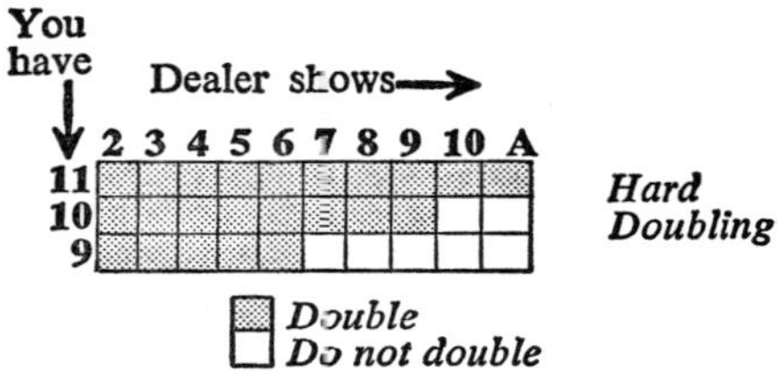

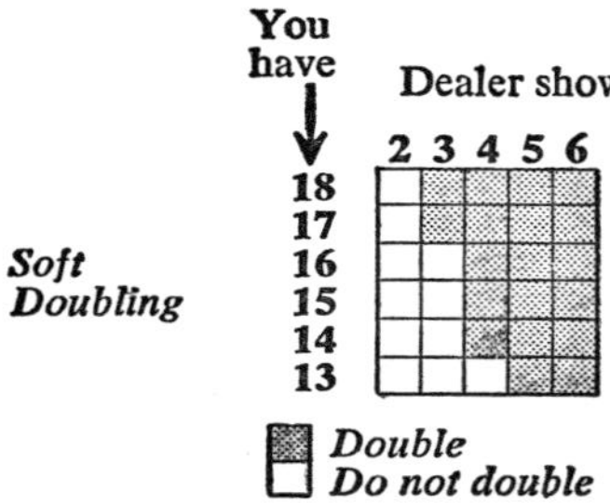

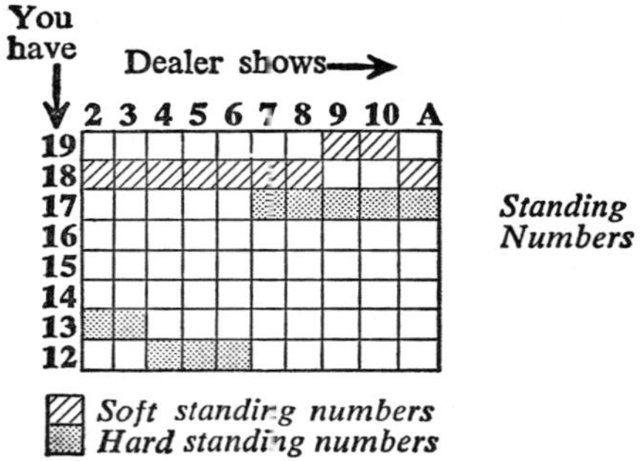

Now that we have the complete standard strategy before us, we can get an over-all insight into it. For this purpose we need Table 3.9, which shows the player's average over-all advantage or disadvantage for each up card of the dealer.

TABLE 3.9. *Player's Over-All Advantage or Disadvantage.*

Dealer shows	**2**	**3**	**4**	**5**	**6**
Player's advantage*	0.094	0.130	0.176	0.229	0.236

Dealer shows	**7**	**8**	**9**	**10**	**A**
Player's advantage*	0.145	0.056	—0.040	—0.105	—0.089

* This is the player's advantage averaged over all the situations when the dealer does *not* have a natural. If he has a natural, insurance is offered, the bet is settled at once, and there is no occasion for using the strategy. When the effect of the dealer's naturals are included in Table 3.9, the player's average advantage when the dealer shows an Ace becomes —0.364. When he shows a Ten, the new figure is —0.172.

If we list the dealer's up cards from left to right, with the cards most favorable to the player on the left and the less favorable, on the right, we get from Table 3.9: *6,5,4,7,3,2,-8,9,A,10*. There now turns out to be an "order of favorability" of dealer's up cards that is closely related to, but not identical with, the order given in the above list. This "order of favorability" is: *5,6,4,3,2,7,8,A,9,10*. It was chosen so that the farther to the left a card is on the list, the more likely a player is to split a pair, double down, or stand. The farther to the right a card is, the less likely it is that the player will do these things. We will refer to cards farther to the left as "more favorable" for the player or as "less favorable" for the dealer.

The reason why the Ace is not the most favorable up card for the dealer, as shown in this list, is that we have assumed that the dealer has already checked his hole card and has found that he does *not* have a natural. The basis for our assumption is that when the dealer has a natural, bets are settled at once and the strategy tables are not used.

On referring to Table 3.8, you see that the hard standing numbers are lowest for *5,6*, or *4*. Thus, from the player's point of view, these are the most favorable up cards the dealer can have. The probability of the dealer's busting with the *5,6*, or *4* is so great that the player should stand on hard 12, taking no risk at all. Up cards of *3* and *2* are not quite as favorable for the player and the hard standing number against them is slightly higher, 13. The group, *7,8,A,9,10* is even less favorable; the hard standing number is considerably higher, 17.

The soft standing numbers have a similar pattern. The soft standing number is always 18 except when the dealer shows *9* or *10*. Then it becomes 19. This corresponds to the fact that 9 and 10 are the dealer's most favorable up cards.

The pattern in the other parts of Table 3.8 is also related closely to the favorability order. Notice that in every case but that of not splitting Nines when the dealer shows a Seven or an Ace, not doubling down on hard Ten against an Ace, and that of not doubling down on *9,2* against an Ace, the rule is that if a thing is done against a certain favorable up card, it is done against all up cards that are still more favorable for the player. If it is not done against a certain unfavorable up card, it is not done against any of those that are still more unfavorable for the player. This explains, for example, much of the soft doubling down pattern. It also shows that splitting Fours against a Five is not an irregularity.

What to Expect When Using the Basic Strategy

You are now familiar enough with the basic strategy to try it out in actual play. If a casino is not available and you play at home, be sure that the set of casino rules we have adopted are in force. This will mean a considerably different procedure than is usually employed in a home game, but perhaps your friends will go along in the interests of learning something new about the game.

The following data may encourage you to try the basic strategy at the casinos, in spite of the fact that when you use it you are still, in general, simply playing about even with the house. Table 3.10 describes the possible outcomes that can be expected if one hundred hands (generally from thirty minutes to one and one half hours playing time, depending on the speed of the dealer and the number of players at the table) are played at $1 per hand and also if a thousand hands (generally from five to fifteen hours of playing time, depending on conditions) are played at $1 per hand. If you bet a different amount per hand, just multiply all dollar values by an appropriate number. For example, if you bet $5 per hand, multiply by 5 and if you bet $0.50 per hand, multiply by 0.50 (or divide by 2). The average loss after one thousand $1 bets is $2.10. After one hundred $1 bets, the average loss is a mere 21¢.

TABLE 3.10. *Results Using the Basic Strategy.*

If 100 hands are played at $1 per hand—

approximate per cent of time that	the result is* between	and
0.01	$19.8	above
0.1	14.8	$19.8
2.1	9.8	14.8
13.6	4.8	9.8
34.1	−0.2	4.8
34.1	−5.2	−0.2
13.6	−10.2	−5.2
2.1	−15.2	−10.2
0.1	−20.2	−15.2
0.01	below	−20.2

If 1000 hands are played at $1 per hand—

approximate per cent of time that	the result is* between	and
0.01	$61.1	above
0.1	45.3	$61.1
2.1	29.5	45.3
13.6	13.7	29.5
34.1	−2.1	13.7
34.1	−17.9	−2.1
13.6	−33.7	−17.9
2.1	−49.5	−33.7
0.1	−65.3	−49.5
0.01	below	−65.3

* Negative numbers indicate losses.

Baldwin *et al.* [3] report the following results with their strategy (it is almost identical with the basic strategy).

TABLE 3.11.

Number of hands played	Gain
930	\$38.50
770	−56.00
1140	−4.50
690	−4.00
3530	−\$26.00

The number of hands played in each group is near enough to 1000 so that if we pretend the number of hands played is 1000 each time in Table 3.11, we can use the second part of Table 3.10 for a rough check of the results of Table 3.11. Everything is normal except for the swing of −\$56. This swing, if it were not the result of causes other than chance, is a rare event. If 770 hands are played at \$1 per hand, the probability that the player will lose \$56, or more, turns out to be approximately 0.01 per cent; that is, the odds against this are about 10,000 to 1.

Comparison with House Percentage Against Other Blackjack Strategies and in Other Games

We remarked earlier that the basic strategy is better than any other published blackjack strategy and that it is also better than any published strategy for any other gambling games. Tables 3.12 and 3.13, respectively, illustrate how much better it is.

TABLE 3.12. *The Basic Strategy Compared with Other Blackjack Strategies.*

Blackjack strategy	Player's advantage (in per cent)
basic	− 0.2 is typical but may reach + 0.3
card experts [7]	− 3.2
mimic the dealer	− 5.7
typical casino player	− 2.00 to − 15.00

TABLE 3.13. *The Basic Strategy Compared with Best Play in Other Casino Games.*

Game	Player's advantage (best play) (in per cent)
blackjack, basic strategy	– 0.21 is typical
craps	– 1.40
roulette (Europe)	– 1.35
roulette (United States)	– 2.70 to – 5.26
bacarrat and chemin-de-fer	– 1.11 to – 5.00

4

A Winning Strategy

Gamblers soon learned through experience that the games of chance could be run in such a way that a certain "percentage" favored one side at the expense of the other side. That is, if a game were played a sufficient number of times (the "long run"), the winnings of the favored side would generally be near a certain fixed percentage of the total amount of all bets placed by the opponent. The modern gambling casino takes the side of the gambling games which has proven in practice to be favorable. If necessary, the casino alters the rules of the game so that the casino advantage is sufficient to cover expenses and yet yield a desirable rate of profit on the capital that the owners have invested.

The total amount of bets placed is called "action." For example, if I place bets of $3, $2, and $11, I have "$16 worth of action." A player who has a certain amount of capital can generally get many times that amount in action before ultimately losing his capital to the house. This contributes greatly to the excitement of gambling.

Failure of the Popular Gambling Systems

There have been many attempts to overcome the casino advantage. A frequent approach has been to vary the amount that is bet from play to play according to various methods, some of which are simple and some of which are very complex. By way of illustration, in the Small Martingale, better known as the "doubling-up" system, the player makes an initial bet of, say, $1. If he loses, he bets $2. Then he wagers $4, $8, $16, and so on, doubling the bet each time *until* he wins. Then the process is repeated starting with $1 again. The bet placed following a string of losses equals the entire amount lost in the string, *plus* one. A winning bet either is a $1 bet, or has been placed after a string of losses. Thus each win results in a net profit of $1, counting from just after the last win, and the player keeps winning a dollar every few bets. However, this system has a flaw. The casino always sets a limit to the amount that may be bet. Suppose the limit is $500 and we have started by betting $1. If there is a string of nine losses ($1, $2, $4, $8, $16, $32, $64, $128, $256), the next bet called for by the "doubling-up" system is $512, and this bet is not permitted.

It seemed in practice that, with this limit on bets, the casino won the same percentage of the action it normally wins, even though a player was using the doubling-up system. Thus the doubling-up system provided no advantage whatsoever to the player. The other complicated betting schemes all seemed to have the same flaw. It was no surprise then when it was later proven, by using the mathematical theory of probability, that for most of the standard gambling games no betting scheme can ever be devised that will have the slightest effect upon the casino's long-run advantage.

The games for which this is an established fact include

those games that are called "independent trials processes" by mathematicians. (Craps and roulette are such games.) What this means is that each play of the game is uninfluenced by past outcomes and, in turn, has no influence on future outcomes. For example, suppose we shuffle a deck of cards and draw one card, which happens to be the Four of Spades. We now return this card to the deck and shuffle *thoroughly.* If we draw one card again, the chance that it will be the Four of Spades is no greater than, and no less than, the chance of it being any one of the other 51 cards. This fact has made popular the phrase "the cards have no memory."

Importance of the Dependence of Trials in Blackjack

In opposition to the previous discussion, in casino blackjack the cards do have a memory! What happens in one round of play may influence what happens both later in that round and in succeeding rounds. Blackjack, therefore, might be exempt from the mathematical law which forbids favorable gambling systems.*

Suppose, for example, that the four Aces appear on the first round that is dealt from a fresh, thoroughly shuffled

* This discussion has been oversimplified for the nontechnical reader. For the reader with a background in probability, we note that, in fact, the mathematical law states that no matter whether trials are dependent or independent you cannot beat the odds, subject to the tacit assumption that the odds are correctly calculated—as conditional probabilities if necessary. It is here that even the casinos with rules unfavorable to the player have blundered. In such casinos the (absolute) probability for a blackjack player to win is slightly under 1/2. Since $\Pr\{\text{win}\} = \sum_{S} \Pr\{\text{win}/S\}\Pr\{S\}$, where the sum is S over all situation, it could happen that the conditional probabilities are all less than 1/2 too. But in fact some of them are considerably greater than 50 per cent, yet casinos still pay even money in those situations. Obviously the dealers who insist on early shuffles are dimly aware of this error. (They could also avoid it by adopting the rule that the players must stick to constant bets between shuffles.)

deck. After that round is over, the cards are placed face up on the bottom of the deck and the second round is dealt from the remaining unused cards. Now on the second round no Aces can appear; there will be no blackjacks, no soft hands, and no splitting of Aces (splitting Aces is highly favorable to the player). This situation of having no Aces in play (which is, on the average, almost 3 per cent against the player as we shall see later) continues in succeeding rounds until the deck is reshuffled and the Aces are brought back into play.

A few years ago one casino made a practice of removing four Tens and a Nine from the deck. From our calculations, we know this added 2.5 per cent to their advantage. This deception was spotted by the Nevada Gaming Control Board and the casino was brought to trial. Eventually the casino's license was revoked. However, there was one ironic sidelight to the trial. The casino operators were practical men through and through and not at all theoreticians. They knew that their short deck helped them but they did not know how much. Thus, they had no answer for the damning assertion of an expert witness that they were putting the player not at a 2.5 per cent disadvantage but at a 25 per cent disadvantage!

The Use of Favorable Situations

The winning strategies to be given in this book depend on the fact that, as the composition of a deck changes during play, the advantage in blackjack will shift back and forth between player and casino. The advantage often ranges beyond 10 per cent for one side or the other and on occasions even reaches 100 per cent. The winning strategies depend, for the most part, on exploiting this fact. We watch the cards that are used up on the first round of play. The fact that these cards are now missing from the deck will, in general, shift the house advantage up or down with regard to those hands which will be dealt on the second round from the now depleted deck.

As successive rounds continue to be dealt from the increasingly depleted deck, and the advantage shifts back and forth between player and house, we make large bets when the player has the advantage and very small bets when the house has the advantage. The result is that the player usually wins a majority of his large favorable bets and, although he generally loses a majority of his small unfavorable bets, he has a considerable net profit.

Here is one very special example of a favorable situation that would be uncovered by a careful count of the cards that are played. Suppose you are playing the dealer "head on"; this means that you are the only player at the table. Suppose also that you have been keeping careful track of the cards played and you know that the unplayed cards, from which the next round will be dealt, consist precisely of two Sevens and four Eights.* How much should you bet? Answer: place the maximum bet the casino will allow. Even borrow money if you have to, for you are certain to win if you simply stand on the two cards you will be dealt.

Here is the analysis. If you stand on your two cards, you do not bust and are temporarily safe. When the dealer picks up his hand, he finds either (*7,7*), (*7,8*), or (*8,8*). Since his total is below 17, he must draw. If he holds (*7,7*), there are no Sevens left so he will draw an Eight and bust. If he holds (*7,8*) or (*8,8*) he will bust if he draws either a Seven or an Eight—the only choices. Thus the dealer busts and you win.

This brings us to the central problem that I had to solve in analyzing the game of blackjack: How can a player evalu-

* The essential thing is that there be at least three Eights and at most two Sevens actually *available for play*. For example, if the casino does not deal the last card (a frequent practice), two Sevens and three Eights would not work in this example.

ate the depleted deck in general to determine whether or not it is favorable, and if it is favorable, precisely how much? This problem was solved by asking the IBM 704 high-speed electronic computer a series of questions. The first question was: Suppose blackjack is played with a deck from which only the four Aces are removed. What is the best possible strategy for the player to follow and what is the house (or player) advantage? In other words, the computer was to do exactly the same as was done in finding the basic strategy, with one exception: solve the problem with a deck which has the four Aces missing.

The result was noteworthy. On playing with a deck that had four Aces missing, the player was at a disadvantage of —2.72 per cent, under best play. It might seem that the removal of the four Aces should affect matters much more than removing any other four cards, since Aces play such a unique role in the deck. They are essential for a natural and for soft hands, and they make the most favorable pair. Wherever they appear, they seem to help the player. Thus it might seem to some players that fluctuations in the proportion of Aces in the deck would have a much greater effect on things than fluctuations in the proportion of any of the other cards and that we ought simply to study Aces alone. However, we will see that Aces alone are not overwhelmingly important.

The computer was asked now to compute the player's advantage or disadvantage, using the best strategy, when playing with decks made up in turn by removing four Twos, four Threes, etc. The results for these and some other special decks are listed in Table 4.1. The corresponding best strategies were computed but have been omitted to save space.

Table 4.1 suggests that a shortage of cards having values *2* through *8* might give the player an advantage, while an excessive fraction of such cards might hurt the player. Conversely, a shortage of Nines, Tens, and Aces ought to hurt

TABLE 4.1. *Player's Advantage or Disadvantage for Certain Special Decks.*

Description of deck	Advantage (in per cent) with best strategy
complete	– 0.21
Q(*1*) = 0	– 2.72
Q(*2*) = 0	1.42
Q(*3*) = 0	1.89
Q(*4*) = 0	2.36
Q(*5*) = 0	3.29
Q(*6*) = 0	1.87
Q(*7*) = 0	1.25
Q(*8*) = 0	0.05
Q(*9*) = 0	– 0.91
Q(*10*) = 12	– 2.15
Q(*10*) = 20	1.89
Q(*10*) = 24	3.94
Q(*1*) = 0, Q(*10*) = 24	0.70
two decks	– 0.42
complete, soft 17 rule	– 0.34

Key: Q(X) = Y means that a particular deck was altered by changing only the quantity Q of cards that have numerical value X so that there are now Y such cards. For example, Q(2) = 3 would mean that in the deck there are now only three Twos instead of the usual four. "Two decks" means the cards are dealt from two ordinary 52 card decks that have been mixed together as one. "Complete, soft 17 rule" means one complete deck but the dealer's rules are altered so that he *draws* on all totals of soft 17.

the player while an excess of them should help him. A variety of winning strategies may be based on counting one or more types of cards. A good, simple winning strategy is based on counting the Fives. It will be described in detail in the rest of this chapter. The readers who find the basic strategy in Chapter 3 difficult should plan to adopt the Five-count strategy as their first winning approach to the game.

On the other hand, that great majority of readers, who learned the basic strategy promptly, should probably plan to use the Ten-count strategy of the next chapter as their first winning approach to the game. It offers many advantages over the Five-count strategy with only a moderate increase in the level of difficulty. These readers probably should not spend a great deal of time practicing the Five-count strategy. However, since the various discussions in the remainder of this chapter are important to the later strategies, it should also be thoroughly read and understood by those who are going on to the Ten-count strategy.

A First Winning Strategy: Counting Fives

Table 4.1 shows that when four cards of one kind are removed from the deck, the greatest shift in the relative advantages of player and house is caused by removing the four Fives from the deck. The effect is even greater than when the four Aces are removed. More important, removing the Fives gives the advantage (3.29 per cent) to the player.

Now, suppose that the depleted deck contains no Fives, but does contain enough cards for the next round of play, and that therefore no Fives will appear during the next round of play. It can be shown that these situations may be considered as mathematically identical with those that arise when hands are dealt from a deck which is complete except that the four Fives have been removed. Without attempting to give the detailed explanation for this, we simply point out that this means that if the player knows that no Fives can appear on the next round of play, and if he then follows what we shall call the "Five-count" strategy, on that round of play he will enjoy the 3.29 per cent advantage that is given in Table 4.1.

The Five-count strategy is given in Table 4.2. The format is that of Table 3.8.

Observe that the Five-count strategy is very similar to the basic full-deck strategy, thus easing the burden on one's memory. In particular, note that the soft standing numbers are the same, that all the basic doubling-down situations also call for doubling down when the Fives are gone, and that the same statement is true for pair splitting except that a pair of Sixes is not split against a dealer's up card of Seven.

TABLE 4.2. *The Best Strategy When It Is Only Known That No Fives Can Appear on the Next Round of Play.**

Pair Splitting

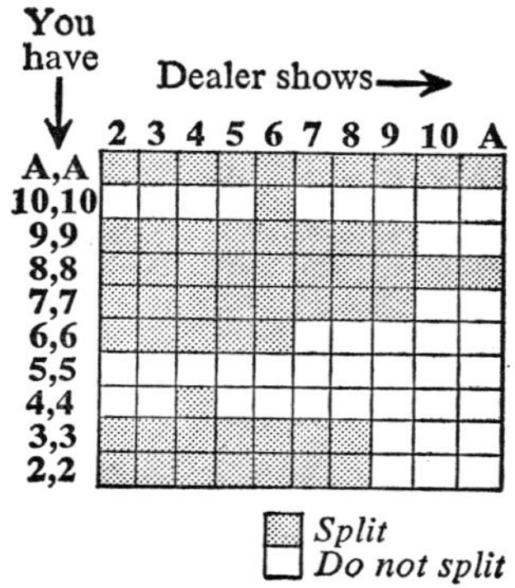

Hard Doubling

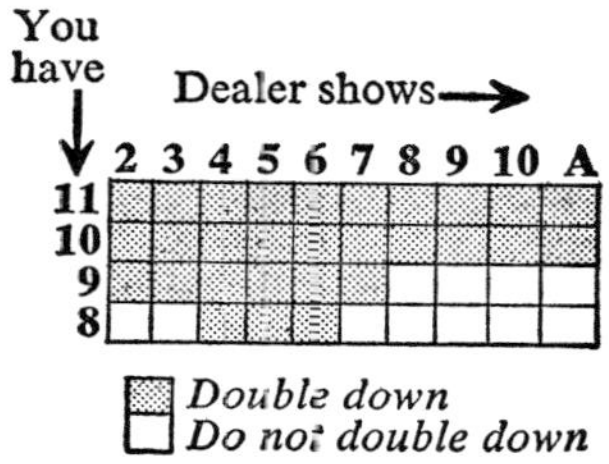

Soft Doubling

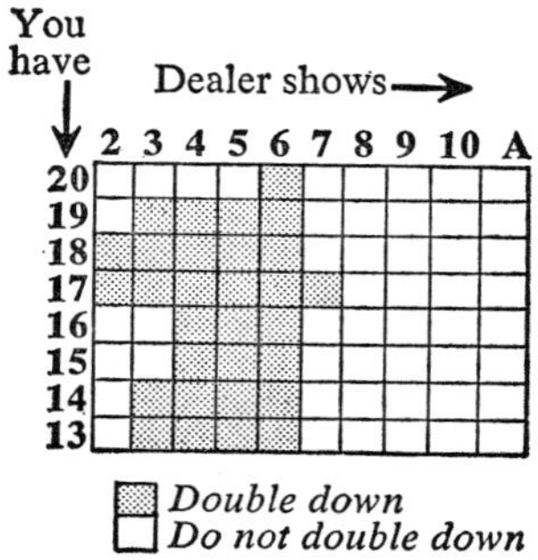

Standing Numbers

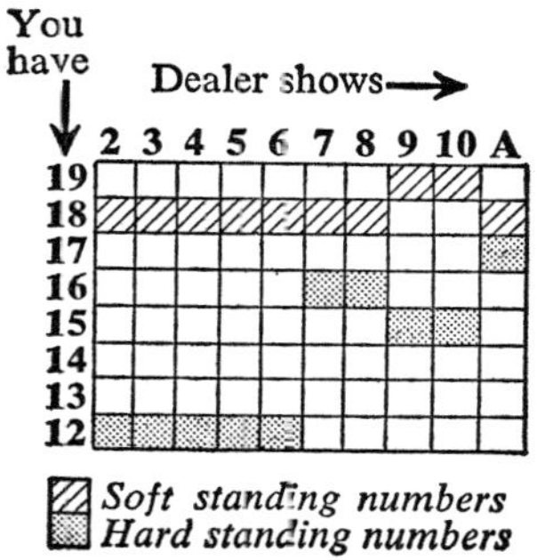

* The row *5,5* in the pair strategy and all columns headed by (a dealer's up card of) Five are meaningless as no Fives can occur. These fictional squares have been included so that the format is identical with that of Table 3.8. We have tried to shade them in such a way that the table is easier to memorize.

As a matter of fact, when all the Fives are gone it is perfectly acceptable to use only the changes in the hard standing numbers and otherwise play according to the basic strategy. The errors thus introduced primarily involve neglecting to split pairs or double down in several instances. Their effect is quite small. The player's advantage is decreased from 3.29 to 3.13 per cent, a change of only 0.16 per cent. I suggest using this approach to the Fives strategy to decrease the load on one's memory. We shall adopt this simplified strategy in all our calculations and discussions of the Fives strategy.

In the rest of the book, we shall use the 3.3 per cent figure when talking of the simplified strategy as well as for the exact strategy. This is justified as follows. Because of certain minor approximations used by the computer, all strategies in this book very probably give a true advantage of about 0.3 per cent more than we claim. Thus, the approximate strategy probably even gives a little more than a 3.3 per cent advantage.

We now outline a simple method for winning at casino blackjack. Begin by making "small" bets and using the standard strategy. Watch the cards that are played and keep track of the Fives. When you see that all four of them have been used, check to see that the next round of play will come entirely from the remainder of the deck, and thus that no Fives will appear.

Now you must place your bet before any of the cards are dealt in this next round. However, you know that you have better than a 3 per cent advantage on whatever you bet. Therefore, place a bet that is "large" in comparison to the ones you have been placing. When the cards are dealt, employ the $Q(5) = 0$ strategy.

We have been recommending that if the Fives are used up before a certain round is dealt, the player should make a large bet and use the Fives strategy. Now it may happen that some Fives remain when a round of play begins and that all of them appear during that round. At the instant this happens the player should change to the Fives strategy. For example, suppose he is dealt hard seven and the dealer shows a Two. Suppose that when the player draws he receives the last remaining Five. He now has hard twelve. The basic strategy says to draw. However, the Fives strategy now applies and according to it, he should stand.

This is to be considered a refinement and is not essential for winning with the Fives strategy. It improves the player's chances of winning some of his small bets, namely, some of those placed at the beginning of the round on which the last Fives appeared.

Suppose that you continue over many deals to place large bets when $Q(5) = 0$, and small bets otherwise. In those situations in which you made large bets, you win in the long run at a rate of above 3 per cent. With your small bets, you lose at a rate of about -0.5 per cent.* If the large bets are big enough compared to the small bets and if the favorable situations occur often enough, the profits from the big bets should both offset the losses from the small bets and leave a comfortable over-all profit.

There are several questions that we must now answer in detail in order to make our instructions complete.

(1) How can you tell whether the remaining cards will be adequate for the next round of play?

*One might wonder why, in the Fives strategy, the small bets do not lose merely at the rate of -0.21 per cent, the average loss rate using the basic strategy. The reason is that small bets are no longer made when the Fives are absent. Thus some favorable situations are removed from the small-bet realm and the remaining small-bet situations are, overall, slightly less favorable than average. The figure -0.5 per cent is inexact. The figure ranges from -0.5 to -0.23 per cent, depending on the number of players at the table. We selected a single number to simplify discussion. We made it as pessimistic as possible.

(2) How often do favorable situations arise?

(3) How much larger than the small bets should the large bets be?

(4) How fast will you make money?

(5) How much risk is there?

(6) How much capital is required to start?

We will take these up in the order listed.

Counting the Cards

The check as to whether the remaining cards are adequate can be made in several ways. The surest way is to actually count how many cards have been used in play. For example, after each round, you might say to yourself something like, "Eleven cards have been played, and I have seen one Five." Count every card that is used as "played" but only count the Fives that you have seen. For example, if a card is burned, be sure to count it whether or not you see what it is. It is not necessary that you see every card that is used in play. If, however, you miss seeing some of the played cards, in those cases that some of them were Fives, you may miss some favorable situations. For example, suppose after a certain round you see that seventeen cards have been played and that three Fives have been used. Suppose also that a Five has been burned and that you do not know this. Then, as far as you know, one Five may yet appear so you will make a small bet and miss the opportunity of exploiting a favorable situation.

If your dealer habitually conceals the burned card, you may wish to request that he show it to you. It is sometimes difficult to know whether to make this request. It should not be made if you think that it will arouse the casino's suspicions that you are playing one of our winning strategies, for they may take countermeasures that are more costly to you than not seeing the burned card.

If the casino does not use the last card, incorporate this into your count from the beginning. The reason for this is that the particular count, when subtracted from 52, is supposed to give the number of cards yet to be played. Table 4.3 is a rough guide as to when the remaining cards will fail to be adequate for the next round.

TABLE 4.3.

Number of players	Remaining cards usually adequate if count of used cards is no more than:
1	45
2	41
3	38
4	34
5	31
6	27
7	24

Counting the used cards has advantages besides that of telling the player whether the unused cards are adequate for the next round. First, the training in card counting is preparation for the more powerful and, also more difficult, winning systems to be presented in succeeding chapters. Secondly, the count is an invaluable asset in the detection of cheating because a common device is to remove one or more cards from the deck. (One might wonder at this point whether casinos have also tried adding cards to the deck. I have only seen it done once. It is very risky. Imagine the shock and fury of a player who picks up his hand and sees that, not only are both his cards Fives, but they are also both spades!)

Another well-known method of cheating which can often be detected by a card counter is called the "turnover." Though the name is apt, the experience is not a dessert treat. In the weak form of the turnover, the dealer watches to see whether the first half of the deck seems to favor the house strongly. If it does not, he continues normally, hoping that the latter half will. However, if the deck does favor the house during the first half, he secretly turns the deck over so that the used cards are on top and are replayed during the second half. In the strong form of the turnover, the dealer stacks the used cards from the first half of the deck as he picks them up after play. When the deck is about half used, he turns it over and deals out stacked hands!

The unwary player generally does not remember which cards he has just seen. However, if the used portion contains a number other than 26 cards, the total deck will seem, to one who counts cards, to contain twice the number in the used portion instead of 52 cards. Further, even if the used portion contains 26 cards, the fraud may be detected unless it also contains two Fives. For the number of Fives in the total deck also seems to be, to one who is counting them, twice the number in the used portion.

For those readers who do not want to count the used cards, there is an alternate, but less satisfactory, method that is frequently adequate for determining about how many cards remain to be played. It can be used if the dealer checks to see how near the end of the deck he is. He does this by pushing the lower cards slightly forward, so that the upper edge of all the cards show slightly. Then the used cards, which are face up, appear "whiter" than the unused cards—provided that the unused cards, which are face down, do not have borders, so that their edges look dark. The relative thickness of the two portions makes it easy to estimate the number of unused cards remaining.

If you have a deck without borders, place a portion of the deck face up underneath the remainder. Then skew the deck by pushing the bottom cards forward slightly. There should be a clear line of demarcation between the two portions. From this, you can estimate the amounts in each portion. With a little practice you can become quite skillful. If you attempt the same thing with a deck having borders, it is harder since the clear line of demarcation usually does not appear.

Here is a warm-up experiment that can be done with any deck; it should convince you that estimating the number of cards in a portion of the deck is not so difficult. First, square the deck by striking its edge against a smooth table top. Now try to break the deck into two equal portions. If necessary, transfer cards from one portion to the other until they appear equal. *Do not* place the two stacks side by side on the table top and match their height. That would destroy the purpose of this experiment, which is to introduce you to judging by eye estimates alone. After a few attempts you will find that rarely, if ever, are you "off" more than two cards. Many people soon learn to divide the deck into two precisely equal parts almost every time.

Frequency of Favorable Situations

The rate at which money is won depends upon how often favorable situations arise and is influenced by how many players are at the table. This dependence is shown in Table 4.4.

It clearly strengthens the player's advantage, when using the Fives strategy, to play in games in which there are no more than five players.

Variations in Bet Size

The instinctive answer to the question, "How much larger than the small bets should the large bet be?" is "As large as possible," for it is the large favorable bets that are responsible for the profit. However, there are some circumstances that need to be considered.

If a player goes along steadily betting $1 and then suddenly, every once in a while bets $500, he may soon be the

TABLE 4.4. *Variation in the Number of Known Favorable Situations, When Fives Only Are Counted, as a Function of the Number of Players.*

Number of players	Number of times Fives are gone per hundred hands	Average amount in large units, won per hundred hands
1	9.8	0.30
2	5.9	0.18
3	6.5	0.20
4	3.5	0.10
5	6.0	0.18
6	0.9	0.03
7	1.7	0.05

object of study by the casino operators. If he is winning, they will very likely take countermeasures. One simple and effective method is to shuffle the deck after the player has made his large bet and before any cards are dealt. Although the player can then remove his large bet, his favorable situation is destroyed.

Thus, it seems judicious to reduce the size of the bet variation to a level that does not attract so much attention. My personal preference is to make the large bets no more than eight or ten times the size of the smaller bets. Let us run through a simple calculation to see how costly this is.

Suppose we are playing 100 hands per hour head on with the dealer. Then, according to Table 4.4, there are 9.8 favorable situations at 3.29 per cent (3.29 per cent advantage because the Fives are gone) in favor of the player and 90.2 unfavorable ones at 0.5 per cent in favor of the house. For simplicity, we shall speak of 3.3 per cent instead of 3.29 per cent. Then, if we are betting \$1 and \$500, we lose $0.005 \times 90 \times \$1$, or 45¢, on the unfavorable situations and gain $0.033 \times 10 \times \$500$, or \$165 on the favorable situations, for a net profit of \$164.55. If instead we bet \$50 in the unfavorable situations, we would lose $0.005 \times 90 \times \$50$ or

$22.50 in these instances but would again win $165 in the favorable situations for a net profit of $142.50.

It should be emphasized that these profit figures are average amounts for a very large number of hands. In any brief series of a few hundred hands, there will very likely be considerable deviations from these figures.

We can now use these figures to estimate the average hourly wage for the Fives system. Suppose that we are playing head on at the rate of 100 hands per hour. We saw previously that we make an average of about $140 per hour when our bets range from $50 to $500. Therefore, we should make $14 per hour when we bet from $5 to $50. The player who only bets from 50¢ to $5 will make a modest $1.40 per hour.

One skilled player whom I know asserts that he can play 350 hands per hour when playing head on. When betting from $1 to $500, he would average $165 × 3.5 or $577.50 per hour, since he is playing 3.5 times as fast as the figure we used before of 100 hands an hour. Thus it is in the system player's best interest to be able to play as rapidly as possible. When more players are present, the fraction of hands that are favorable dwindles. Furthermore, since it takes longer to play out a round, each player gets fewer hands per hour.

The Problem of Gambler's Ruin

We have yet to answer the last two of the six questions we asked a few pages earlier:

How much risk is there?

How much capital is required to start?

These questions are both facets of a single problem that has been worked out in great detail by mathematicians: the problem of gambler's ruin.

The gambler's ruin problem may be described as follows. Suppose the player has an advantage of A per cent over the house. In the favorable situations of the Five-count strategy, we know that the number A is 3.3; we use a letter here because later we may want to see what happens with numbers greater or smaller than the 3.3 value of A. Suppose also that the player has C units of capital and that he wants to win W units from the casino. In the Five-count strategy, the effect of the small, unfavorable, waiting bets is negligible, as the calculations in the last few pages suggest. Thus we can, for discussion purposes, ignore the effects of the small bets and think of the game as being played at the rate of, say, ten plays an hour (assuming one player playing 100 hands an hour; see Table 4.4) with A taken as 3.3, or for simplicity, 3.0. (Actually, this pessimistic reduction from 3.3 to 3.0 in most cases compensates adequately for the losses from the small bets that we decided to ignore.) In this discussion, a unit means the size of the large bets that are being made during the times of the 3.0 per cent advantage of the Five-count system. Thus, if bets were ranging from $1 to $8, a unit would be $8. The gambler's ruin problem asks "When the numbers A, C, and W have been specified, what is the chance that the player will lose his capital C before winning the desired amount W?"

One point that may be disturbing some readers is how one can lose at all if he has the advantage. First, I must emphasize that "3 per cent advantage" as used in this book means only that if a player makes many thousands of bets, each at a 3 per cent advantage, he will find that his total winnings are close to 3 per cent of the action. This is the principle on which the casinos base their operation. The total action and the total number of plays are generally large enough in even a single day's play so that only rarely will a good-sized casino be behind for that day. However, in a short run of a few dozen or even a few hundred bets, the deviations from this figure may be quite large. In fact, even though the casinos have the advantage over most individual players, one sometimes sees a winner walk away from the tables.

In order to get a feeling for the kinds of fluctuations that may occur, we are going to "play" a game in which the player has a whopping 10 per cent advantage over the casino. We shall do this by using the table of random numbers in Appendix A. These numbers have been carefully designed so that they may be used for this purpose. They show precisely the same irregularities and fluctuations that are characteristic of a game of chance.

In order to play a game having a 10 per cent advantage for the player, we let 55 number pairs (notice that the digits in Appendix A are printed in pairs), say those from 00 through 54, mean a win of one unit for the player and the 45 pairs, 55 through 99, mean a loss. Then in the long run our excess of wins over losses will be about $(55 - 45) \div 100$ or 10 per cent. Now, starting with the first line of Appendix A, we have 11 16 43 63 18 which we will interpret as win, win, win, loss, win. The results of this game are most easily visualized with the aid of a graph. For each win, the graph goes up one step and for each loss it goes down one step. The first five steps, win, win, win, loss, win, will appear as up, up, up, down, up. One hundred plays of the game, using the first hundred pairs of random numbers in our table (by reading each line across), appear in the graph of Figure 4.1. The straight line represents a 10 per cent gain on each and every bet and shows "average" behavior with a 10 per cent advantage.

In Figure 4.1, notice that the line representing the amount the player is ahead wanders unpredictably back and forth. It does not stay very close to the line representing the average expected result. In fact, in this particular case the results are very "bad." At the end of 100 plays, the player is ahead by only two units whereas on the average he would be ahead by ten units.

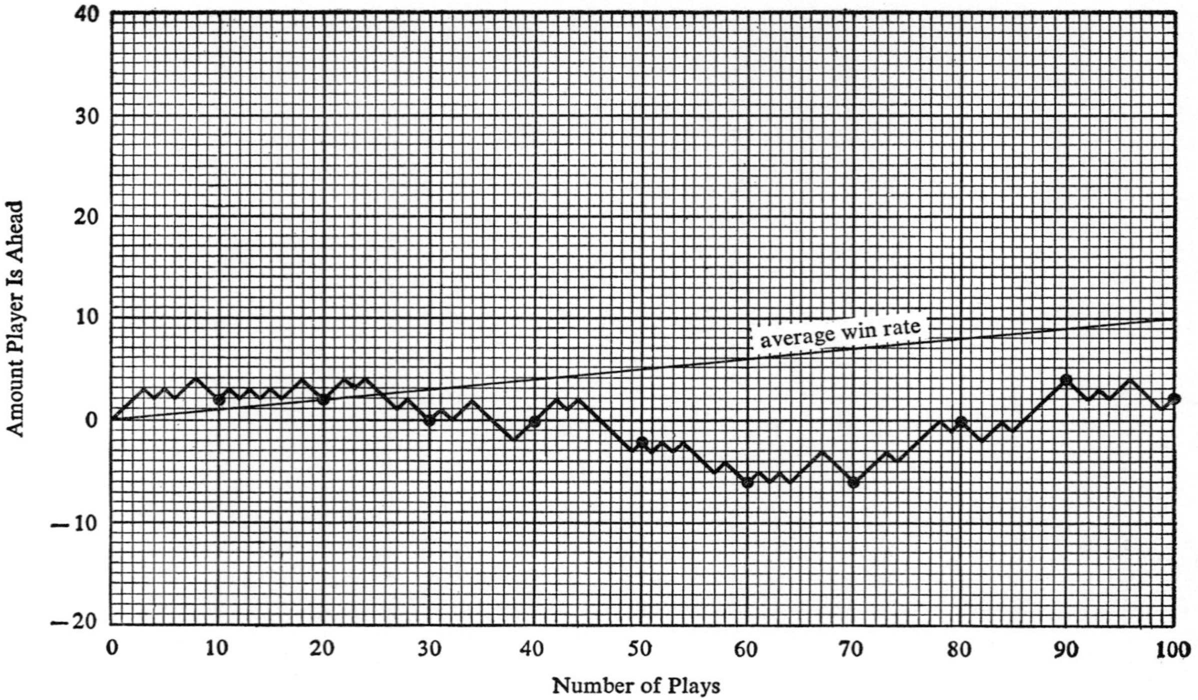

FIGURE 4.1. *Wins and Losses for One Hundred Plays of a Game with $A = 10$ Per Cent Based on Arbitrarily Chosen Random Numbers.*

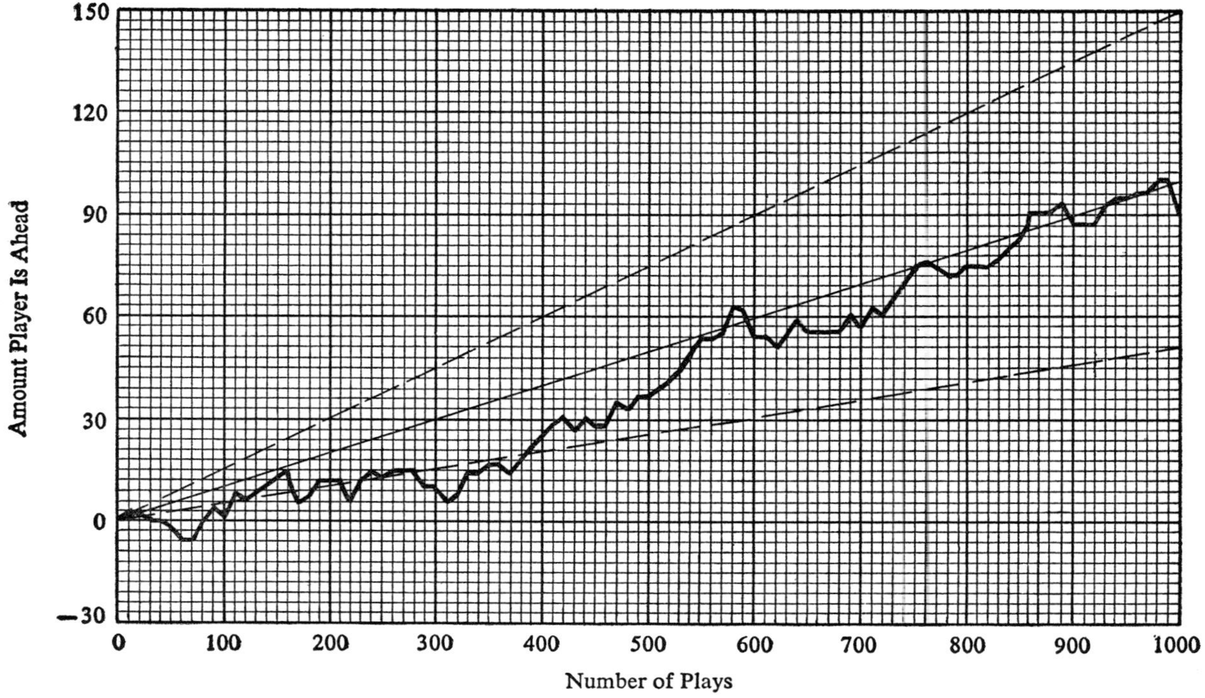

FIGURE 4.2. *Wins and Losses for One Thousand Plays of a Game with $A = 10$ Per Cent Based on Arbitrarily Chosen Random Numbers.*

Originally I chose the first 55 pairs, 00 through 54, to represent a win. This was an arbitrary choice on my part. *Before* I saw the random number table, it would have been equally valid for me to let any 55 of the 100 possible pairs represent a win. For example, if I had chosen the 55 pairs, 45 through 99, as winners, and the 45 pairs, 00 through 44, as losers, the player would be four units above average instead of behind as he is shown to be in Figure 4.1.

In Figure 4.2, the first thousand pairs of numbers from Appendix A have been used (with 00 through 54 again representing a win), to play a game where the player has a 10 per cent advantage. However, points are plotted on the graph only every tenth play. It is as though the player stops to count his pile of chips after each ten plays, and only then. Thus Figure 4.2 is slightly "smoothed out." The first ten points in Figure 4.2 correspond to every tenth point in Figure 4.1, as follows. The heavy dots in Figure 4.1 show how the player stands after each ten plays: 2,2,0,0,–2,–6, –6,0,4,2. These are the first ten points of Figure 4.2 and the other points may be thought of as having been found in the same way.

The greatest downward swing in Figure 4.2 occurs during the first one hundred plays, which, as we have mentioned, is a smoothed version of Figure 4.1. On referring to Figure 4.1, we see that the farthest downward point is –6 and that it occurs four times, at plays 60, 62, 64, and 70. Thus a player who had begun the series of 1000 plays in Figure 4.2 with six units or less would have been ruined by the sixtieth play and would not have been able to go on to build up the 90-unit lead that appears at play 1000. On the other hand, however, a player who started with just seven units would not have been ruined but would have reached play 1000 and, consequently, the 90-unit lead.

We could investigate the ruin problem by using the table of random numbers to play games corresponding to other selected values of the player's advantage. If A is 4 (per cent), for example, we could let any fifty-two pairs, say 01 through 52, be wins and the forty-eight remaining pairs, 52 through 00, be losses. In order to produce a game with a 3.0 per cent advantage, let 01 through 51 be wins and 52 through 99 be losses. Skip 00 if and when it occurs. The player's advantage is given by calculating the equation

[(number of winning pairs) − (number of losing pairs)] ÷
[(number of winning pairs) + (number of losing pairs)]
= A,

which in the last case is (51 − 48) ÷ (51 + 48), or 3.0 per cent. This last game therefore corresponds to playing the Fives strategy.

To investigate further the ruin problem by actually playing out games would require a great many games before we could answer even such a simple question as whether the seven units required to protect against ruin in Figures 4.1 and 4.2 are typical for the 10 per cent advantage game. We would have to play out a great many additional games each time we wanted the answer to some other question. Fortunately a mathematical formula is available to answer these ruin questions for all choices of A, C, and W. For the benefit of those readers who are familiar with algebra, the formula for the chance of ruin (according to [9], page 314) is

$$R = \frac{\left(\frac{1+A}{1-A}\right)^{W} - 1}{\left(\frac{1+A}{1-A}\right)^{C+W} - 1},$$

where again we remind you that A is the player's per cent advantage over the house, W the number of units the player wants to win, and C the number of units of capital he has.

If we assume that the player never quits unless he is ruined, the formula simplifies to

$$R = \left(\frac{1 - A}{1 + A}\right)^C.$$

On applying this to the game we played in which A was equal to 10 per cent (0.1) and C was equal to 7, we find the chance of ruin is

$$R = \left(\frac{1 - 0.1}{1 + 0.1}\right)^7 = \left(\frac{9}{11}\right)^7 = (0.818)^7 = 0.245 = 24.5 \text{ per cent.}$$

Hence the chance of survival is 75.5 per cent. In other words, when we play games in which we have a 10 per cent advantage, in about 75.5 per cent of those games a mere 7 units of initial capital will be enough to save us from being ruined, even if we play "forever." Of course, if ruin is going to come to a player who has the advantage, it generally must come early in the game; for, if the player survives for a moderate length of time he will probably accumulate enough capital to make the chance of future ruin very small. With only 6 units, R equals $(0.818)^6$ or 0.30, which is 30 per cent. Thus only 30 per cent of the time should we be ruined, as we were, starting with six units. This fits in with our earlier observation that the game in Figure 4.1 was a little "unlucky" for us, considering our whopping 10 per cent advantage.

It takes many more units to protect against gambler's ruin for the player who only has a 3 per cent advantage. Since most players probably either do not know algebra or are no longer used to working with it, Table 4.5 lists ruin probabilities in the 3 per cent case for various choices of initial capital and desired winnings.

Within each of the first three sections of Table 4.5, note that the player's initial capital is the same. In the first section

TABLE 4.5. *Player's Chance of Ruin When He Has a Three Per Cent Advantage.*

		Probability of	
C	W	Success	Ruin
10	∞	0.456	0.544
10	20	0.543	0.457
10	10	0.647	0.353
20	∞	0.704	0.296
20	40	0.723	0.277
20	20	0.772	0.228
50	∞	0.952	0.048
50	100	0.952	0.048
50	50	0.954	0.046
1	∞	0.059	0.941
2	∞	0.114	0.886
3	∞	0.167	0.833
4	∞	0.217	0.783
5	∞	0.263	0.737
6	∞	0.307	0.693
7	∞	0.347	0.653
10	∞	0.456	0.544
15	∞	0.599	0.401
20	∞	0.704	0.296
25	∞	0.782	0.218
30	∞	0.839	0.161
40	∞	0.912	0.088
50	∞	0.952	0.048
60	∞	0.974	0.026
70	∞	0.986	0.014
80	∞	0.992	0.008
90	∞	0.996	0.004
100	∞	0.998	0.002
200	∞	0.999995	0.000005

Key: C, player's initial capital (units). W, number of units player is trying to win; ∞, the mathematical symbol for infinity, means the player is trying for an unlimited sum of money.

each capital unit is ten; in the second, twenty; in the third, fifty. The player's goal, however, is changed from infinity to twice the player's initial capital and then to an amount just equal to the player's initial capital. In each section, the ruin probability falls off as the player reduces the size of his goal, relative to the amount of his initial capital. Since, within the rest of this book, we shall assume that the player is out to win as large an amount as possible, we shall thus work with the case W equals infinity. In case a ruin probability for a specific C is not listed in the table it can be obtained easily as follows from those that are given. For example, if the ruin probability for $C = 13$ is desired, multiply the ruin probability for C equal to 3 by that for C equal to ten (or for any other values of C that add up to thirteen); the result is then 0.833×0.544, or 0.454.

From Table 4.5, we see that when the player's advantage is 3 per cent, it takes between 20 and 25 units (the actual figure is 23) to give the same 75 per cent protection against ruin that only 7 units gave when the player's advantage was 10 per cent. However, if we increase our basic capital to 40 units, Table 4.5 shows us that the chance that we can play forever, winning arbitrary sums of money—all the money on earth if the game could be prolonged indefinitely—is more than ten times the chance that we will be ruined instead. With 200 units protection, the odds in our favor jump to 200,000 to 1.

Capital Required, Extent of Risk, Rate of Profit

We will now use the remarkable facts just given to answer the questions:

How much capital is required to start?

How much risk is there?

What is the average rate of profit?

First you must decide how much your initial capital will be. You must NEVER, NEVER play with money that it will hurt you to lose. Besides the usual arguments against this, there is one more: playing with money that you cannot afford to lose produces psychological disintegration, bad play, and consequently a greater chance of defeat. Conversely, playing with money that means little to you leads to cool confidence and devastatingly accurate play.

Now that you have cut down your stake to a sensible level, the next decision you must make is how small you want to make your chance of ruin (that is, loss of your stake). Suppose you choose 5 per cent. Then, by Table 4.5, if you wish to win large amounts, you require 50 units. (If you had instead accepted a 40 per cent chance of ruin, you would need only 15 units.) Suppose your stake is $1000. Dividing this into 50 equal parts gives a unit size of $20. This is the size of your large bet. Choose some convenient size for the small waiting bets—say $2 or $3. Consulting Table 4.4, you see that the average win rate with just one player at the table is 0.3 units per hundred hands dealt, which for this example, amounts to $6.

If you play instead with the 15-unit stake and a 40 per cent chance of ruin, you need only $300 to make the same $6 per hour average profit—that is, if you survive ruin. Furthermore, the $1000 stake, divided into 15 units of about $67 each, would bring in an average of $20 per hundred hands played. Thus, for any one size of stake, there are a variety of choices open to the player. If he wants to play boldly, taking a large chance of being ruined, he can make a comparatively large amount per hour. On the other hand, the player may divide the stake into so many units that there is virtually no chance of ruin. However, the price paid for this is a considerable reduction in average profit.

5

A Winning Strategy Based on Counting Tens

The strategy to be discussed in this chapter, the "Ten-count" strategy, has several advantages over the Five-count strategy. The most important of these is that, given exactly the same stake and the same ruin probability, the Ten-count strategy will win money several times as quickly. The advantages this strategy finds for the player generally range from 1 to 10 per cent. The large advantages yield heavy winnings. The smaller advantages give the player camouflage: it turns out to be natural in this strategy to vary the bet size with the advantage in small steps all the way from the small, waiting bets to a size perhaps ten times these bets. This is less conspicuous than making essentially two types of bets, "large" and "small."

Another camouflage advantage of the detailed Ten-count strategy is that the player's decisions depend strongly on the composition of the remaining cards. Suppose for example the dealer has an Ace up. Sometimes the player should hit hard 17; other times he should stand on hard 12!

One might wonder, in view of Table 4.1, how a strategy based on Tens could give greater advantages than one based on Fives. Card for card, Fives have more effect than Tens: four Tens added to the deck give the player an advantage of 1.89 per cent whereas four Fives removed from the deck give an advantage of 3.29 per cent. The solution is that there are 16 Tens in the deck and only four Fives. Thus much greater deviations from the average can occur in the number of Tens than in the number of Fives.

Effect on Player's Advantage as Proportion of Tens Varies

The richer the deck is in Tens, the better off the player is, generally. We shall now think of the deck as divided into two types of cards, "Tens" and "others." During play, we shall keep track of the number of others and the number of Tens that have not yet been seen. Thus, with the Tens strategy, we take into account only the cards we see, as we see them. From these two numbers we shall determine "Ten richness" by computing the ratio "others/tens (others *to* tens)." For example, suppose the complete deck is shuffled and prepared for play. For the complete deck, the "count" is 36 others and 16 Tens, or simply (36,16). The corresponding ratio is 36/16 or 2.25. The player's advantage for various values of the ratio others/Tens is shown graphically in Figure 5.1. The approximate advantages for several ratio values are given in Table 5.1 for quick reference.

Learning to Count

Our first goal will be to learn to keep count of the others and Tens yet to be played while also playing with the standard strategy. Here is an exercise which should be done as a preparation in learning to count. Take a shuffled com-

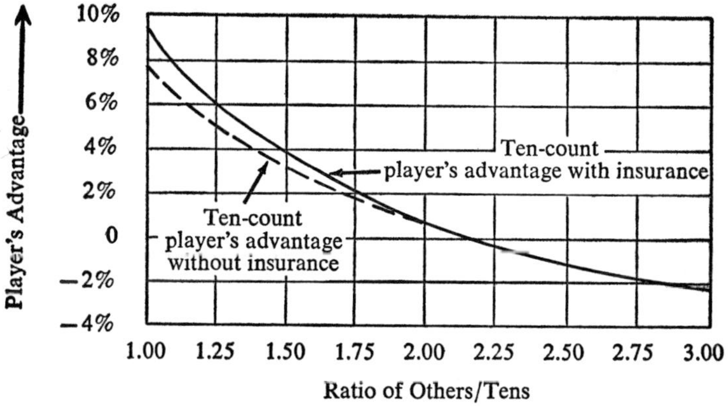

FIGURE 5.1. *Player's Advantage for Various Values of Others to Tens.*

TABLE 5.1. *Approximate Player Advantage in the Ten-Count Strategy.*

Others/Tens	Normal approximate advantage (in per cent)
3.00	− 2.2
2.25	− 0.2
2.00	1.0
1.75	2.0
1.63	3.0
1.50	4.0
1.35	5.0
1.25	6.0
1.16	7.0
1.08	8.0
1.00	9.0

plete deck and, turning cards over one at a time, "count" them, and drop them face up onto a discard pile. For example, I have just picked up the deck on my writing desk. I count, "(36,16); *3* of Spades (35,16); *5* of Clubs (34,16); *3* of Hearts (33,16); *4* of Diamonds (32,16)—the ratio is now 2.00 and the hands dealt now give the player a 1 per cent advantage (Table 5.1); *3* of Diamonds (31,16); *6* of Spades (30,16); Queen of Diamonds (30,15), etc." A few cards from the end of the deck, stop and record your count. Then see if the remaining cards agree with your count of them. In the example above, when I stopped my count was (2,1) and the last three cards were the deuce of Clubs, the Nine of clubs, and the King of clubs, in agreement with the count.

The first few times it may take you two minutes or more to go through one deck without any mistakes. However, you should be able to drop your time, in six or eight fifteen-minute practice sessions, to between twenty-five and fifty seconds. Fifty seconds is more than adequate and twenty-five seconds is excellent. I had trouble getting below twenty-five seconds until I found that it takes me twenty to twenty-five seconds to turn over the cards, whether I count them or not. For those who want to push this exercise to the limit, there is a way to break this twenty-five second barrier. Remove a few unknown cards and spread the remaining cards face up in a row, with enough of each card showing so that it may be easily identified. Then count, by reading either from left to right or from right to left. You should learn to be equally at ease reading in each direction. Your count should check against the unknown cards that were removed.

Shortly after I had practiced spreading the cards for rapid counting, there was an opportunity to use this skill. I was examining a certain casino to see if it cheated and began, naturally, by watching the table where the most money was being risked. After the shuffle, it was the casino's practice to have the dealer place a joker face-up on the bottom of the deck to separate the used cards from the unused ones. At the end of one deal the joker had vanished! The amazed players asked to examine the deck. The dealer spread it in the standard fashion and then scooped it up again in about four seconds. Even with the rapid count I could only count the first 12 cards.

The players demanded a closer look at the deck. This time the dealer gave them ten or fifteen seconds. When I reached 38 cards (28,10), the dealer began to slowly scoop them up again. I hastily counted the number of remaining cards without regard for denomination. There were twenty left: the deck had 58 cards! Of course the dealer still had not allowed the players enough time to examine the deck. Therefore they called for a new deck and requested that the pit boss examine the old one. He counted the old deck off to one side, holding it in his hands in such a way that no one else could count along with him. When he finished counting, an odd expression flickered over his face. Then he left, without offering a word of explanation to the players about the recent puzzling events, taking the old deck with him.

While you are increasing your counting speed with this exercise you should also practice maintaining a count while someone deals to you and you play the standard strategy. Have them deal slowly enough so that you can count easily even though you may be painfully slow at first. Play with chips and start with 200 units. Before each hand, use your count to estimate the ratio. Then vary your bets according to the scheme given in Table 5.2.

Roughly speaking, whenever the ratio is between 2 and

TABLE 5.2. *A Conservative Betting Scheme for the Ten-Count Strategy.*

Ratio	Bet, in units
above 2.00	1 (minimum)
2.00-1.75	2
1.75-1.65	4
1.65-1.50	6
1.50-1.40	8
below 1.40	10

1.40, we are betting about twice as much, in units, as our advantage is in per cent. We level off below 1.30 at 10 units so the variations in our bet size will be less extreme. You do not need to perform a division in your head to figure out the ratio exactly. Rough guesses, say to within 0.1 or even 0.2, are very satisfactory.

Insurance

There is one important change from the standard strategy that you should take into account at once. Whenever the ratio is less than 2.00, take insurance if the opportunity (dealer's up card an Ace) presents itself. (A discussion of insurance was given on p. 12.) If the ratio is 2.00 or more, do not insure. This is reasonable. If the deck is Ten-rich and the dealer shows an Ace, he is more likely than usual to have blackjack. You are allowed to check your hole cards (and you may have been able to see other player's hole cards too) before insuring. You have also seen the dealer's up card. All this can be taken into account, if you wish, before deciding whether to insure. You do not need to perform a division in your head to decide whether the ratio is below 2.00. Simply multiply the number of Tens that remain by two. If the results exceeds the number of others, insure. If it does not, then do not insure.

We can calculate either the player or the house advantage from the insurance bet whenever we know the number of Tens and of nonTens. We illustrate this calculation for the case when hands are being dealt from the complete deck, a situation which turns out to accurately represent the average house advantage. In this instance, the dealer's up card is an Ace, and since the dealer's Ace is visible, there are 51 possibilities for the dealer's hole card (assuming at the moment, for simplicity, that we do not use our knowledge of our own two hole cards as well), 16 of which are Tens. On the average, the player wins twice the amount of his insurance wager 16 times out of 51, or 31.4 per cent of the time. The bet is lost 35 times out of 51. The average house edge is $35/51 - 2 \times 16/51$, which is $3/51$ or 5.9 per cent.

If you wish to take into account your hole cards, there are three cases to consider. If your hole cards consist of *(10,10)*, the house edge is $35/49 - 2 \times 14/49$, which is $7/49$ or 14.3 per cent. If they consist of *(10,x)*, where *x* represents a nonTen, the house edge is $34/49 - 2 \times 15/49$, which is $4/49$ or 8.2 per cent. If you hold *(x,x)*, the house edge is $33/49 - 2 \times 16/49$, which is only $1/49$, or 2.0 per cent.

Insurance was originally introduced by the casinos as just one more way of fleecing the player. It is ironic that a bet providing such an average advantage for the casino can be turned against the house. The trick, of course, is simply more of what we have been doing all along. The average house advantage is 5.9 per cent, but there are times when the advantage is in favor of the player. At these times we insure and otherwise we do not. For example, when the count before the deal is (10,10) the player's average profit on an insurance bet is $2 \times 10/19 - 9/19$, which is $11/19$, a healthy 58 per cent of the amount of the insurance.*

When I first played in a certain large and (then) scrupulously honest casino, I noticed that it had no insurance betting. Since one of the owners was standing at my elbow (for I had begun to win rapidly and they had rushed up to stop me), I asked why there was no insurance. He said that because it hurt the players, it was taken out for their benefit. As a large bettor (large bettors generally are humored and given little privileges), I asked that I be allowed to insure, explaining that it gave me a feeling of security when I made large bets (when the count was (10,10) for example!). My

* For simplicity, we neglect knowledge of the dealt cards except for the dealer's visible Ace.

request was refused and without an explanation. I later learned that one player, using end play (discussed later), the insurance rule, and card counting, had taken at least $40,000 from this casino before he was stopped. The dotted line in Figure 5.1 shows how the player's advantage drops when insurance is not allowed.

Many dealers and players alike share two widespread misconceptions about the insurance bet. They often become annoyingly insistent in their attempts to "correct" a player who does not share their view. The first misconception is that a player should always take insurance if possible when dealt a natural. The argument is that if the dealer has a natural also, the hands themselves will tie but the insurance bet wins one unit. If the dealer has no natural, the player's natural wins 1.5 units and his insurance bet of 0.5 unit is lost. Again the win is 1.0 unit. In either case the player has a sure profit of one unit. Why not take it?

First, I will show you that there is a case in which the insurance bet is wasteful. Suppose that you are counting Tens and others and that after you see your hole cards, and before you decide whether or not to take insurance, you find that all ten-value cards have been played. In this event, the dealer cannot have a natural. If you insure your natural, you have a sure profit of exactly 1.0 unit, as discussed above. However, you know that your natural is a winner so if you do not insure, you have a sure profit of 1.5 units. Thus in this instance, to insure is to throw away 0.5 unit.

Now suppose the deck had only one Ten and, say, eight nonTens left. Should you insure? No, because even though your insurance bet might win, you are probably throwing it away. On the other hand, if the remaining cards were entirely Tens, the dealer would be certain to have a natural also and insurance wins for sure 1.0 unit for you. If in imagination we let the deck get richer and richer in Tens, there ought to be some critical point, beyond which insurance is profitable and below which it is unprofitable. It is the same point we recommended above. When the ratio falls below 2.0, insure. When it is above 2.0, do not insure. When it is exactly 2.0, there is, in the long run, no gain or loss on the average so you can do as you please. Actually, in this one instance, to insure a natural will reduce the fluctuations in your capital. Thus, if you have limited capital, there is a minor advantage to doing so.

The same arguments apply, with greater force, to the second misconception, which is "insure a good hand, and do not insure a poor one."

Strategy Tables

There is a complication in giving the Ten-count strategy. For the best possible play, we must vary our strategy as the ratio varies. For each ratio there is a corresponding strategy. Fortunately, all these separate strategies can be combined into a single chart, given in Table 5.4 or, better, in Table 5.3. The difference between Tables 5.3 and 5.4 is that the player using Table 5.4 can count the cards anytime during the play of the hand. This enables him to count them in one or a few large groups and reduces the effort of counting. The player using Table 5.3 keeps a "running count"; that is, he keeps track of the cards as they appear. The effort of counting is considerably greater but the player is compensated in that he is able, with his up-to-the-second information, to play his hands with considerably greater precision. Most readers should be able to learn to count well enough to use Table 5.3. Tables 5.3 and 5.4 have our usual format, with one exception: some of the squares, instead of simply being shaded, have numbers. In the case of doubling down and pair splitting, these numbers are to be interpreted as follows. If the ratio is equal to or less than the number in the square, consider the square shaded; that is, split the pair or double down. If the ratio exceeds the number in the square, consider the square blank; that is, do not split the pair or double down. There are two numbers marked with an asterisk(*). These numbers have an opposite interpretation. If the ratio is greater than or equal to such a number, consider the square shaded. Otherwise, consider it blank.

Referring to Table 5.3, read the minimum standing number chart as follows. The soft standing numbers are the same as for the basic strategy except when the dealer's up card is an Ace. In that case, it is 18 as usual for ratios of 2.2 or less. It is 19 for ratios above 2.2. The hard standing number against an Ace is 17, as usual, if the ratio is less than or equal to 3.1 (but greater than 1.4). For ratios above 3.1 it is 18. The hard standing number for up cards of *2* through *10*, and for an Ace when the ratio is 1.4 or less, is read, as follows, from the chart. For a given ratio, shade all squares having numbers greater than or equal to that ratio. The lowest shaded square is the correct standing number. Alternately, one might think of all the squares with numbers greater than or equal to the current ratio as the goal. Draw until your total equals or exceeds the totals represented by these squares. For example, if the dealer shows a *4*, the standing numbers are: 12 for ratios of 2.2 or less; 13 for ratios above 2.2 but less than or equal to 2.6; 14 for ratios above 2.6 but less than or equal to 3.3.

Notice that the hard standing numbers against cards *2* through *6* have all dropped to 12 by the time the ratio drops to 2.0, which is the point at which we begin increasing our bet size. You may recall that the hard standing numbers for cards *2* through *6* were also all equal to 12 for the Five-count strategy. As the ratio becomes larger, which corresponds to a shortage of Tens, these hard standing numbers rise. They reach seventeen against a *2* when the ratio is above 3.9 and against a *3* when it is above 5.0.

The most important part of this strategy to incorporate into your plan is the standing numbers chart. This gives you

TABLE 5.3 *The Ten-Count Strategy, Based on the Value of the Ratio When a Running Count of the Cards Is Kept.*

Pair Splitting

You have ↓ / Dealer shows →	2	3	4	5	6	7	8	9	10	A
A,A						3.7	3.0	2.9	3.2	2.5
10,10	1.5	1.6	1.7	1.8	1.8					
9,9	2.3	2.7	2.9	3.5	2.9	1.6	3.5	4.1		1.5
8,8									1.5*	2.7
7,7							3.3			
6,6	2.3	2.6	2.9			3.7				
5,5										
4,4	1.3	1.5	1.8	2.3	1.9					
3,3	5.5						2.5*			
2,2	3.0									

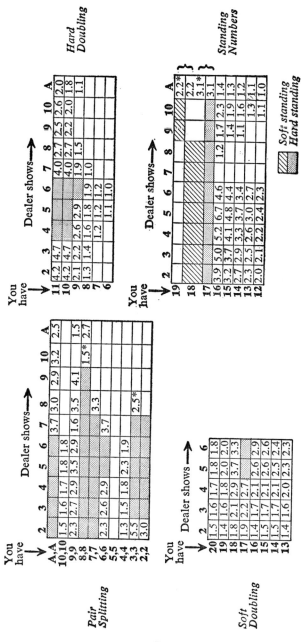

Hard Doubling

You have ↓ / Dealer shows →	2	3	4	5	6	7	8	9	10	A
11	4.2	4.7				4.0	2.7	2.5	2.6	2.0
10	4.2	4.7				4.0	2.7	2.2	2.0	1.8
9	2.1	2.2	2.6	2.9		1.9	1.5			1.1
8	1.3	1.4	1.6	1.8	1.9	1.0				
7			1.2	1.2	1.2					
6				1.1	1.0					

Soft Doubling

You have ↓ / Dealer shows →	2	3	4	5	6
20	1.5	1.6	1.7	1.8	1.8
19	1.4	1.6	1.8	2.0	2.0
18	1.8	2.1	2.9	3.7	3.3
17	1.9	2.2	2.7		
16	1.4	1.7	2.1	2.6	2.9
15	1.5	1.7	2.1	2.6	2.6
14	1.5	1.7	2.1	2.5	2.4
13	1.4	1.6	2.0	2.3	2.3

Standing Numbers

You have ↓ / Dealer shows →	2	3	4	5	6	7	8	9	10	A
19										2.2*
18										2.2, 3.1*
17										3.1
16	3.9	5.0	5.2	6.7	4.6		1.2	1.7	2.3	1.4
15	3.2	3.7	4.1	4.8	4.4			1.4	1.9	1.3
14	2.7	2.9	3.3	3.7	3.4			1.1	1.6	1.2
13	2.3	2.5	2.6	3.0	2.7				1.3	1.1
12	2.0	2.1	2.2	2.4	2.3				1.1	1.0

Soft standing (hatched) / *Hard standing* (shaded)

Numbers followed by (*) are read in reverse fashion: Split (*8,8*) against a *10* when the ratio is *above* 1.5 and not otherwise. Split (*3,3*) against an *8* when the ratio is *above* 2.5 and not otherwise. Against an Ace, the soft standing number is 19 if the ratio is above 2.2. It is 18 if the ratio is 2.2 or less. The hard standing number against an Ace is 18 when the ratio is above 3.1. It is 17 when the ratio is 3.1 or less.

most of the theoretical advantage. However, if you wish to add other parts of the strategy, the order of importance is the same as in the standard strategy: first, learn hard doubling, then pair splitting, and lastly, soft doubling.

There is one refinement that should be taken into account. It may happen that the cards that appear during the play of the hand seriously change the ratio from what it was when the bet was placed. This effect is generally greatest at the end of the deck, since the number of cards drawn at that time is a comparatively large portion of those remaining. This problem can be ignored at some loss, but it is better to solve it by keeping a "running count" which counts each card as soon as it becomes visible in play rather than waiting until the hand is over. When such a running count is kept, it gives the player great exactness in making decisions. I personally play with a running count, and therefore always use Table 5.3 rather than Table 5.4.

When a running count is used for strategy decisions, changes from the strategy table of Table 5.4 are needed. To see why this is so, consider the following situation. A complete deck is shuffled and (say) a Ten is burned. The count is (36,15), a ratio of 2.4. Suppose the dealer's up card and both of the player's hole cards are others. The running count is now (33,15) with a corresponding ratio of 2.2. Thus the entry of 2.4, in the square of Table 5.4 which describes doubling down with hard ten against an up card of Nine, is 2.2 in Table 5.3. A number of other similar small changes occur.

Memorizing either Table 5.3 or 5.4 in its entirety seems like too much work. When I began play in the casinos with the Ten-count strategy, I only knew approximately the standing number and doubling down parts of Table 5.3. For soft doubles, I knew even less. I played the standard strategy until the ratio fell to 1.4 and then I doubled down on all soft totals from 13 to 20 against cards *2* through *6*.

TABLE 5.4. *The Ten-Count Strategy, Based on the Value of the Ratio* Before *the Deal.*

Pair Splitting (You have ↓ / Dealer shows →)

You have	2	3	4	5	6	7	8	9	10	A
A,A						4.0	3.3	3.1	3.1	2.8
10,10	1.4	1.5	1.6	1.7	1.7					
9,9	2.5	3.0	3.2	3.8	3.1	1.8	3.8	4.5		1.7
8,8									1.5*	3.0
7,7							3.6			1.5
6,6	2.6	2.9	3.1			4.0				
5,5										
4,4	1.4	1.6	2.0	2.5	2.1					
3,3	6.0						2.8*			
2,2	3.3									

Hard Doubling (You have ↓ / Dealer shows →)

You have	2	3	4	5	6	7	8	9	10	A
11	4.6	5.1				4.4	3.0	2.8	2.6	2.2
10	4.6	5.1				4.4	3.0	2.4	2.0	1.9
9	2.3	2.4	2.8	3.3		2.0	1.7			
8	1.4	1.6	1.8	2.0	2.0	1.1				
7			1.3	1.4	1.4					
6				1.2	1.1					

Soft Doubling (You have ↓ / Dealer shows →)

You have	2	3	4	5	6
20	1.4	1.5	1.6	1.7	1.7
19	1.5	1.8	2.0	2.2	2.1
18	2.0	2.2	3.2	4.0	3.6
17	2.1	2.4	3.0		
16	1.6	1.8	2.3	2.8	3.8
15	1.6	1.9	2.3	2.8	2.9
14	1.6	1.9	2.3	2.8	2.7
13	1.5	1.8	2.2	2.6	2.5

Standing Numbers (You have ↓ / Dealer shows →)

You have	2	3	4	5	6	7	8	9	10	A
19										2.3*
18										2.3 / 3.3*
17										3.3
16	4.0	5.1	5.4	6.8	4.7		1.2	1.8	2.1	1.5
15	3.3	3.8	4.2	4.9	4.5			1.4	1.8	1.4
14	2.7	2.9	3.3	3.8	3.5			1.2	1.5	1.3
13	2.4	2.5	2.7	3.0	2.8				1.3	1.2
12	2.1	2.1	2.3	2.5	2.4				1.1	1.1

Soft standing (hatched) / *Hard standing* (shaded)

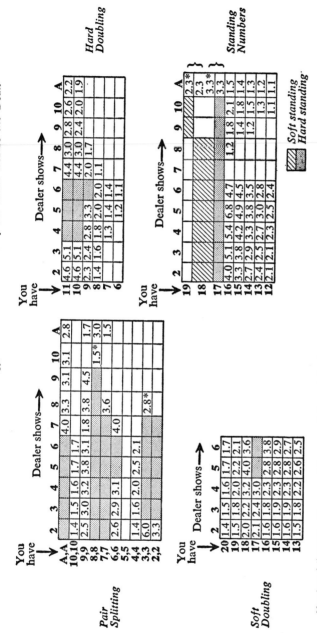

Numbers followed by (*) are read in reverse fashion: Split (*8,8*) against a *10* when the ratio is *above* 1.5 and not otherwise. Split (*3,3*) against an *8* when the ratio is *above* 2.8 and not otherwise. Against an Ace, the soft standing number is 19 if the ratio is *above* 2.3. It is 18 if the ratio is 2.3 or less. The hard standing number against an Ace is 18 when the ratio is above 3.3. It is 17 when the ratio is 3.3 or less.

Time and time again dealers have smiled as though I were insane when I doubled down on soft twenty and turned it into a poor total. But their smiles have disappeared when they bust themselves.

The use of a running count and Table 5.3 often yields large gains over Table 5.4 towards the end of the deck. Suppose, for example, that the count is (6,1), with a corresponding ratio of 6.0, and that we are dealt a hard 9 and the dealer shows a *3*. The running count is now (3,1) and the ratio is 3.0. Table 5.4 would lead us to believe the hard standing number is 17, whereas Table 5.3 shows it is now 15. Suppose we draw a *3*. The count becomes (2,1) and the ratio becomes 2.0. The hard standing number has now dropped to 12, therefore we stop drawing.

The running count sometimes yields gains at the end of the deck because the player can figure out from it what the dealer's hole card is. On a hand I once played in Las Vegas this made a difference of $250. I had bet $125. I glimpsed the other players' hole cards and so, when my turn came (I was the last to play), I knew precisely two cards remained, both Tens. The dealer's hole card was therefore a Ten and only one card, a Ten, remained unplayed. If I were to draw, it would be offered, then the dealer would see it was the last card and as was customary he would pull it back and shuffle. The dealer had a Ten up, thus he had twenty. I had hard 18; if I did nothing I was sure to lose. Therefore, I attempted to draw a card. As predicted, there was only one more card, a Ten, so the dealer pulled it back and shuffled. I attempted to draw again. When I saw my card I almost fell off my chair. It was a *3* for a total of 21 and a winner. When the dealer turned up my cards he was astounded by my draw on hard 18. I was barely able to explain it away by seeming dazed and saying that I had added my cards to 15. When the same situation arose half an hour later, except that I held hard 19 against a sure twenty,

I did not dare draw seeking an Ace (to tie) or a deuce (to win).

When there are other players at the table and you have not been able to see and count some of their cards by the time it is your turn to play, it is profitable, particularly near the end of the deck and when big bets are involved, to make inferences as to what these cards are and to use these inferences to modify your behavior. For example, suppose the count were (9,6) after you saw the dealer's up card and your own cards, you were the fourth of four players, and the first three players stood (without hesitation) on their hole cards. Then the inference is quite strong that they each hold one and perhaps two Tens. Estimating their hole cards to be four Tens and two nonTens, the true count, for purposes of your draw, is perhaps (7,2). Hence, if the dealer is showing an Ace and you hold hard 14, 15, or 16, you should draw, rather than stand. It is even likely that you should draw on hard 17 in this instance!

Learning the Strategy Tables

During the writing of this book, I taught the system to several people with diverse backgrounds and interests. One purpose was to see whether the card-counting methods and charts of this chapter, the key chapter in the book and perhaps the most difficult one, could be readily learned. Without exception, everyone was discouraged when they first saw Tables 5.3 and 5.4 (only one need be learned and I recommend Table 5.3) and when they were told they would have to count the cards. Without exception everyone was surprised at the speed with which they learned. A couple of one-hour practice sessions, with someone else dealing, generally was enough to fix the basic strategy. Two more one-hour sessions were enough to teach the simplified Five-count system. By then almost everyone gets impatient from waiting for the relatively infrequent favorable (Five-less) situations. Two to five additional one-hour practice sessions, plus some counting practice, usually are enough to teach the players to count the Tens and others and to vary their bets accordingly (see Table 5.2) while they are playing the basic strategy. The single remaining problem is memorizing one of the tables. We shall use Table 5.3 to illustrate a method of memorization that was worked out through experience.

The first logical step is to learn the parts of Table 5.3 which have to do with your big bets, namely those parts involving ratios below the average. This information is given in Table 5.4a, a first approximation to Table 5.3 in which the precise Ten-count strategy is played for all ratios below average and the basic strategy is played otherwise. One might think of Table 5.4a as no more than the basic strategy plus some modifications. The learning of Table 5.4a can be broken into several stages. One should begin with the standing-numbers table; it comprises the most important strategy. As is true in most tables throughout this book, this table is most easily learned if one looks for patterns in it. Notice, for example, that the ratio in the squares below the Ace begin with 1.0 and increase one-tenth at a time. Below 9, the change in ratio between squares is three-tenths. Below 10 the changes are not very regular. The changes in tenths are two, three, three, four. Note, however, that the standing number drops from 17 to 16 if the *running-count* ratio drops to 2.3. A very slight excess of Tens is enough to change the standing number. In Appendix II we shall see that in the basic strategy the hard standing number against Ten is just barely 17; the player who uses 16 instead only loses 0.8 per cent.

The next strategy in order of importance is the hard doubling down table. Note that the steps, in tenths, across the eight row are one, two, two, one. Note also that the seven row consists of 1.2 repeated three times. These latter

TABLE 5.4a. *A First Approximation to the Ten-Count Strategy.**

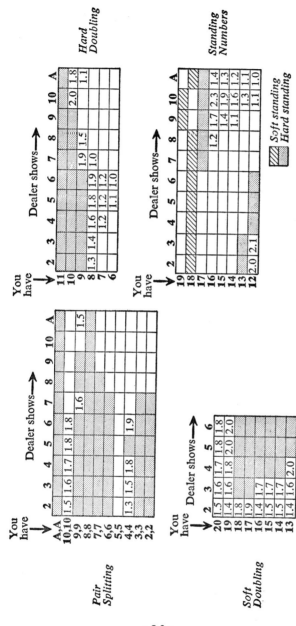

Pair Splitting

You have ↓ / Dealer shows →	2	3	4	5	6	7	8	9	10	A
A,A										
10,10	1.5	1.6	1.7	1.8	1.8					
9,9						1.6				1.5
8,8										
7,7										
6,6										
5,5										
4,4	1.3	1.5	1.8		1.9					
3,3										
2,2										

Hard Doubling

You have ↓ / Dealer shows →	2	3	4	5	6	7	8	9	10	A
11										
10									2.0	1.8
9						1.9	1.5			1.1
8	1.3	1.4	1.6	1.8	1.9	1.0				
7			1.2	1.2	1.2					
6				1.1	1.0					

Soft Doubling

You have ↓ / Dealer shows →	2	3	4	5	6
20	1.5	1.6	1.7	1.8	1.8
19	1.4	1.6	1.8	2.0	2.0
18	1.8				
17	1.9				
16	1.4	1.7			
15	1.5	1.7			
14	1.5	1.7			
13	1.4	1.6	2.0		

Standing Numbers

You have ↓ / Dealer shows →	2	3	4	5	6	7	8	9	10	A
19										
18										
17										
16							1.2	1.7	2.3	1.4
15								1.4	1.9	1.3
14								1.1	1.6	1.2
13									1.3	1.1
12	2.0	2.1							1.1	1.0

Soft standing (hatched)
Hard standing (shaded)

* The Ten-count strategy is used in the large-bet Ten-rich situations and the basic strategy is used as an approximation to the correct strategy in the small-bet Ten-poor situations.

numbers, of course, are for the three dealer's up cards most favorable to the player.

There are not many pair splitting squares to learn. However, the Ten splits are quite important. A player is ordinarily dealt a pair of Tens on about one hand in 11. The frequency is even higher when the ratio drops. Note that Ten-splitting (and also Four-splitting) occurs only against the favorable dealer's up cards of *2* through *6*. Once again there is a sharp division between *6* and *7*. Note also that the steps, in tenths, are one, one, one, zero, in the Ten-Ten row. Also note that the entries in this row are identical with that of the 20 row of the soft-doubling table.

The soft-doubling table can be learned approximately, if desired. Since there are many patterns and many approaches, we shall make a few observations and then leave things to the reader. Note that there are three squares with 1.4. They are all against *2*, the least favorable up card in the group listed in the table. The 1.4's occur with totals of 13,16, and 19 (three, six, nine—easy to remember). All numbers increase as we go from left to right along a row. With the exception of the three 1.4 squares, they also increase as we go down a column from 20 towards 17 or up a column from 13 towards 17.

When most (or all) of Table 5.4a has been learned, the next stage is to get an approximate idea of the hard standing numbers against *2* through *6* when the ratio is high. You probably already will have been "leaning" in these situations.

Further proficiency in the details of Table 5.3 are only for the perfectionist, and need not concern us here.

Figure 5.2 illustrates the improvement in the player's advantage, for various ratio values, as he advances through various stages of learning the Ten-count strategy table. The upper solid curve represents the player's advantage (with insurance) when using fully Table 5.4 or Table 5.3. Those curves are the same as those in Figure 5.1. Actually, the

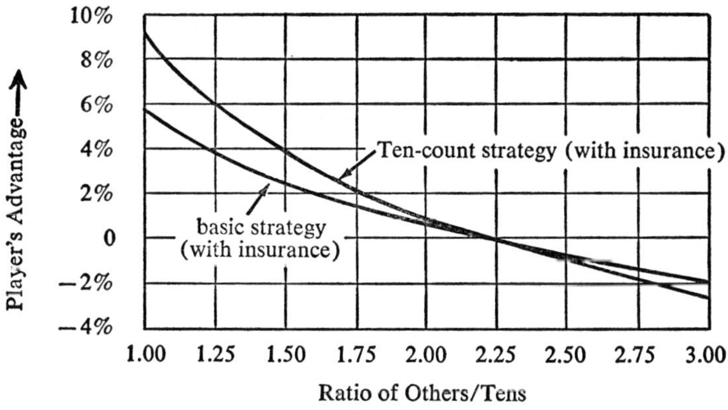

FIGURE 5.2. Ten-Count *Player's Advantage for Various Ratio Values.*

curves for Table 5.3 are even a little more favorable. The solid lower line represents the player's advantage when always using the basic strategy, as we did in the beginning of this chapter. As the player masters more and more of Table 5.4a, the part of the curve representing his advantage for ratios below 2.25 rises from the lower curve until, when he completes mastery of Table 5.4a, it coincides with the upper curve. (Actually, it would slightly exceed the upper curve except that most of us probably would not bother to learn exactly the last few details of Table 5.4a.) Mastery of the standing numbers alone accounts for more than half of the improvement.

As the rest of Table 5.3 is learned, the curve for ratios above 2.25 also advances from the lower curve to the upper curve.

Rate of Profit

The reader by this time should be wondering whether the Ten-count strategy will win fast enough compared to the Five-count strategy, to justify the extra work involved in learning and playing it. We now describe the rate at which the Ten-count strategy wins.

The player's advantage, or lack of it, was calculated and recorded for 1551 hands. The results, which seem to be fairly typical of what arises in actual play, are given in Table 5.5.

TABLE 5.5. *Frequency of Favorable Situations Arising in the Ten-Count Strategy.**

Player's approximate advantage in per cent	Per cent of time this advantage occurred	Per cent of time at least this advantage occurred	Proportional betting: equivalent frequency of 3 per cent situations	Modified proportional betting: equivalent frequency of 3 per cent situations
1-2	10.5	32.0	1.2	1.2
2-3	5.3	21.5	2.4	2.4
3-4	3.9	16.2	3.9	3.9
4-5	4.1	12.3	7.3	5.5
5-6	2.8	8.2	7.8	4.7
6-7	1.2	5.4	4.8	2.4
7-8	0.8	4.2	4.4	1.9
8-9	1.4	3.4	9.9	3.7
9-10	0.3	2.0	2.7	0.9
at least 10	1.7	1.7	18.8	5.7
		total	62.2	32.3

* The situations arising near the end of the deck are often extremely favorable for the player. However, many casinos shuffle a few cards from the end. Hence we have not included any situations involving five or less cards remaining in the deck. These percentages of favorable situations are for one player at the table. However, these percentages only drop to about half their value when there are six players at the table, in contrast with the extreme drop off in the Fives strategy.

Note from Table 5.5 that a player counting Tens has an advantage of 1 per cent or more about a third of the time. It turns out that the advantage ranges between 1 per cent in favor of the player and 1 per cent in favor of the house about a third of the time, and that the house has an advantage of

1 per cent or more about a third of the time. The player has an advantage of 3 per cent *or more* about 16 per cent of the time. This is to be compared with a 3 per cent advantage 9.8 per cent of the time with one player against the house, using the Fives strategy. Further, with the Tens strategy, most of these situations are actually considerably better than 3 per cent.

Study has shown that a scheme for betting which gives very good protection against ruin while also providing a large yield is to risk a percentage of your initial capital equal to your percentage advantage. For example, with $200 and a 3 per cent advantage, bet $6, with a 10 per cent advantage, bet $20, with a 1 per cent advantage bet $2.00; with situations less favorable than 1 per cent, bet a minimum $1. With the Fives strategy, this scheme gives (Table 4.5) 33 units protection and a ruin probability of about 0.13. It turns out that, although many larger bets are being placed in the Ten-count method using this proportional betting method, the larger bets are also safer. The result turns out to be that the ruin probability is still 0.13. However, the win rate is sharply increased. For example, in a 6 per cent situation twice as much money is being bet as in a 3 per cent situation. Twice as much money, all earning at twice the rate, means that there is four times the profit, on the average, in the 6 per cent situations as in the 3 per cent situations. When this is taken into account and the figures in Table 5.5 are used, it is found that the Tens strategy, in conjunction with proportional betting, is equivalent to having 3 per cent situations 62.2 per cent of the time. This compares with a figure of 9.8 per cent with the Fives strategy. Thus

The Tens strategy with proportional betting is more than six times as effective as the Fives strategy!

When more than one player is at the table, the Tens strategy loses somewhat in efficiency but the decline is not nearly as sharp as it is in the Fives strategy. Thus the gain over the Fives strategy is even greater in these instances, so the above statement is true in general.

With \$200 capital and bets of \$1 to \$20, the average rate of winning with the Tens strategy for one player at the table is about $62.2 \times 0.03 \times \$6 = \$11.20$ per hundred hands. With the Fives strategy it is about $9.8 \times 0.03 \times \$6 = \$1.76$. In both cases the ruin probability is about 0.13. With \$400 and the same bet sizes, the ruin probability drops to 0.017. With only \$100 and still keeping the same bet sizes of \$1 to \$20, it rises to 0.36. Of course, with only \$100, if the bet sizes are cut by half and so range from \$0.50 to \$10, then the ruin probability drops to 0.13 again but the rate of profit falls to half, \$5.60 per hundred hands.

In the tests of this system on which I report in the next chapter, modified proportional betting was used: 1-unit minimum when my advantage was below 1 per cent, 2 units with a 1 per cent advantage, 4 units with a 2 per cent advantage, and so on, up to 10 units with a 5 per cent advantage. Above 5 per cent all bets were levelled off at 10 units to reduce the possibility of frightening the casino. This precaution turned out to be insufficient in several of the casinos.

Columns three and four of Table 5.5 compare the effectiveness of this modified proportional betting and straight proportional betting. Suppose that the same amounts are bet in each system when the advantage is 5 per cent or less, and that the bets above 5 per cent in the modified proportional betting are held to the 5 per cent level, or 10 times the minimum bet. Then a comparison of the column three and column four totals suggests that modified proportional betting is just a little over half as effective as proportional betting. However, for a fair comparison it should be noted that the ruin probability for a given initial stake using modified proportional betting is, under these circumstances, somewhat less than for proportional betting. If we increase the bet sizes for modified proportional betting enough so that the two ruin probabilities are equal, there is an increase in the rate of winning with modified proportional betting. The result is that modified proportional betting is only a little poorer than proportional betting.

There is a variation on the proportional betting schemes of the foregoing discussion which is mathematically superior to them but involves a little extra mental work. This variation is sometimes called the Kelly gambling system [18], or "fixed fraction" betting. In it, the player bets an amount proportional to his *current* capital. The amount bet should be equal to or slightly *less* than the player's percentage advantage. For example, suppose a player has $200 when a 10 per cent situation arises. He bets $20. Suppose he wins. He now has $220. Suppose the next situation offers a 6 per cent advantage. He would then bet 6 per cent of $220 or $13.20. However, since bets involving $0.20 generally are not allowed, the player should bet $13, the nearest whole number amount *less than* $13.20.

Notice that if the player has a very bad run, he keeps reducing his bets under this system. This makes it very difficult for him to be ruined. If money were infinitely divisible and there were no minimum, ruin would be impossible. On the other hand, if he gets ahead, his bets are increased and thus he takes advantage of his expanded capital. It is a curious fact that (on even money bets) the player with an advantage should bet a percentage of his capital just equal to his percentage advantage. The player who continues to bet several times this amount will almost certainly be eventually ruined. The player who bets less than this amount will prosper, but not as greatly.

The principle of ruin as a consequence of overbetting is very well illustrated in the simple card game of "Acey-Deucy," frequently played in the Armed Forces. The game begins with each player putting an "ante" in the "pot."

The top two cards of a shuffled deck are placed face up, side by side. The "first player" may wager against the pot any amount, up to the amount in the pot, that the next card turned over will fall "between" the two exposed cards. Ace is high and deuce is low; hence the term "between" may be interpreted as strictly between, meaning that the card turned over must be unequal to either of the two face up cards, lower than the higher ranking and higher than the lower ranking. Or, between may be interpreted as allowing equality also, depending on the game. If the "first player" does not bet the pot on a given hand, further bets are taken, proceeding to the left of the first player until either the pot is covered (i.e. the total amount of bets made equals the amount in the pot) or until all players have had an opportunity to place bets. If the players lose, their bets augment the pot. If the pot decreases to zero, the players ante again. The privilege of being "first player" rotates to the left on successive hands. A number of situations favorable to the individual player arise here. However, most players who are quick to spot this tend to "overbet"—that is, they bet a percentage of their capital greater than their percentage advantage. To their amazement they lose their modest capital even though they have made a series of bets, each of which is favorable to them.

For the twenty-one player whose capital is unlimited to the extent that he is not concerned with the gambler's ruin problem, the greatest average profit may be obtained by betting the maximum whenever his advantage is, say, 1 per cent or more, and betting much less—perhaps one tenth as much—when his advantage is, say, below 1 per cent. The average win rate under these circumstances, estimated from the figures of Table 5.5, is $535 per hundred hands. In actual play, this last betting scheme leads to wild fluctuations. At the end of one or a few hours play the deviation from the average expected win is often several thousand dollars. However, more often than not, the player is well ahead.

Considerable improvements in results can be obtained with the Tens strategy by taking into account two additional factors: the effect of Aces and what we call "end play." We shall first discuss the effect of Aces.

Including Aces in the Count

According to Table 4.1, when the four Aces are removed from the deck, the house advantage is 2.72 per cent. However, since the remaining count is 32 others and 16 Tens, the ratio is 2.00. For this ratio, Table 5.1 gives an average player advantage of about 1 per cent. This may also be expressed as a house advantage of −1 per cent. Thus, in this instance, the absence of the four Aces causes a swing in favor of the house of (2.72 per cent) − (− 1.00 per cent), or 3.72 per cent, away from the average situation we would expect. Again from Table 4.1, when there are no Aces but eight extra Ten-value cards have been added to the deck, the player's advantage is 0.7 per cent. But the ratio is 32/24 or 1.33.* This ordinarily gives an advantage of about 5 per cent so here the swing in favor of the house is about 4.3 per cent. It seems reasonable then to subtract about 4 per cent from your estimated advantages whenever you notice that the Aces are gone.

When the deck has an excess of Aces (i.e., is Ace-rich),

* With one deck, 24 Ten-value cards can never be present since there are only 16 in the entire deck. In a two deck game this situation can arise, however. Further, the results of the computer calculation showed that the player's advantage depends primarily on the ratio and only very slightly on the absolute numbers of others and Tens. Thus counts of (32,24), (28,21), (24,18), (20,15), (16,12), (12,9), (8,6) (4,3) as well as innumerable larger counts, all give a ratio of 1.33 and all have very nearly the same best strategy and all give very nearly the same advantage to the player. This is assuming that the proportions of other cards are fixed throughout.

the player's advantage is correspondingly increased. To illustrate with some extreme cases, suppose the unused cards consist exclusively of Aces and Tens. (In my experience, I have seen the last eight cards happen to all be Aces and Tens.) How much should you bet? If possible, bet one half of your capital; save the other half for pair-splitting or insurance. If the dealer has an Ace up, you can insure and prevent him from winning in case he has blackjack.

If you lost your insurance, the dealer must have a pair of Aces and must bust when he draws; therefore you will win your main bet. If he has a Ten up, he may have an Ace under and, consequently, have blackjack. A part of the time you, too, will hold blackjack and the game will be a standoff. The rest of the time you will lose, but this is the only time you lose. If the dealer has no blackjack, he has a Ten under also. Then with *(A,10)* you win; with *(10,10)* you can tie or, if any Aces remain, you can split your Tens with the chance of a net gain. With *(A,A)* you can split for a sure win if there are cards remaining. If the deck is exhausted, splitting *(A,A)* against the dealer's *(10,10)* keeps your average loss fairly small.

The foregoing discussion is included to make it seem reasonable that when hands are dealt only from a collection of Aces and Tens, the player is greatly favored. A detailed mathematical analysis confirms this. Even when there are too few Aces and Tens to finish the hand, and the deck will have to be shuffled in the middle, the player generally has the edge. For example, when the last three cards to be dealt* are *(10,10,10)*, the player's edge is at least 43 per cent. When they are *(10,10,A)*, in some unknown order, of course, his average profit is at least 100 per cent of his bet.

* This analysis applies directly only when the casino deals down to the last card. However, if the last card is not played, and there is a four-card residue consisting of Aces and Tens, the three cards actually played will be one of the sets we consider; thus the analysis extends.

When they are (*10,A,A,*), his advantage is at least 73 per cent. Only in the case of (*A,A,A*) does the player have a disadvantage; it is then 20 per cent or less. This case is so rare, compared to the other three, that it may be neglected. Of course, the player does not actually count on these situations for winning money; they are entirely too rare. In a casino that practices dealing down to the last card (so favorable to the card-counting player), only about once in a thousand hands will a player face a three-card residue consisting of Aces and Tens.

As you become comfortable with the Ten-count strategy, you can begin to keep track of Aces. When the deck has an excess of Aces, increase your bet somewhat over that which is called for in the straight Tens strategy. On the other hand, bets should be reduced when the deck has a scarcity of Aces (is Ace-poor). An excess or scarcity of Aces may be determined by using Table 5.6. The table shows the curious fact that, in most instances, it is impossible for an average number of Aces to be left: there must be either a shortage or an excess.

You must be more careful than ever, when counting Aces and Tens, to avoid letting the casino know that you are keeping track of the cards. A story about a friend of mine illustrates what not to do. This friend was counting both Tens and Aces and betting from $1 to $200. As a result he was winning heavily. After a while, he made a maximum (for him) bet of $200, since his count showed a very favorable situation. He was dealt a pair of Tens. As yet, there was one Ace unseen. The dealer had a Ten showing but did not have a natural. My friend had seen the burned card and knew that it was not an Ace. Since there was only one unused card left in the pack, it had to be the remaining Ace. Furthermore, this casino was at that time dealing the last card (the customary practice now is to withhold the last card and to place it with the used cards and

TABLE 5.6. *Excess or Shortage of Aces in the Deck.*

Number of cards left	Number of Aces left 0	1	2	3	4
51-40	S	S	S	S	E
39	S	S	S	A	E
38-27	S	S	S	E	E
26	S	S	A	E	E
25-14	S	S	E	E	E
13	S	A	E	E	E
12-1	S	E	E	E	E

Key: E *excess of Aces;* A *average number of Aces;* S *shortage of Aces.*

shuffle). Now, placed in a situation such as this, knowing you would get the last card, an Ace, if you requested it, what would you do? Draw? Split the pair of Tens? My friend asked to double down on his $200 bet. Pityingly, the dealer attempted to explain to this "foolish free spender" that he must have wanted to split his Tens. They argued until finally the pit boss was called over to settle the confusion. Now both the dealer and the pit boss pleaded with my friend, in an attempt to "save him from himself." By this time, a crowd of employees as well as spectators had gathered. Finally, infuriated and exasperated from the long haggle, my friend yelled, "Give me the g-- d----d Ace!" The card was dealt. It was an Ace. The amazed pit boss paid the $400 and then escorted our hero to the door. Of course, he was barred from further play in that casino.

The effect of Aces can be taken into account rather precisely. The idea is to estimate the relative Ace-richness of the deck and then to add a correction to the advantage that is computed from the ratio of others to Tens. We have seen that no Aces means a correction of — 4 per cent (see page 91). For example, suppose there are 26 cards remaining, among them all four Aces. According to Table

5.6, the average number of Aces is two. The average number can also be computed from $(26/52) \times 4$. Thus in this case the number is double the average so a correction of 4 per cent should be added. If, for example, the 26 cards consisted of 16 others (including 4 Aces) and 10 Tens, the ratio would be 1.6 and the player's advantage would normally be about 3 per cent according to Table 5.1. (There a 3 per cent advantage is listed for 1.63 but the difference between 1.6 and 1.63 is small so the advantage for 1.6 is close to 3 per cent.) However, with the 4 per cent correction for Ace-richness we get a figure of 7 per cent for the player's advantage. If instead the 26 cards consisted of 19 others (including 4 Aces) and 7 Tens, the ratio would be 19/7 or 2.7. Interpolating,* we find that the normal approximate advantage is $[(2.7 - 2.25)/(3.0 - 2.25)] \times [-2.2 - (-0.2)] - 0.2 = [0.45/0.75] \times [-2.0] - 0.2 = -1.2 - 0.2 = -1.4$ (per cent). But the correction for Ace-richness is, in this instance, $+4$ per cent so the actual player advantage is $4 - 1.4$ or 2.6 per cent. Again, suppose 20 cards remain and there are three Aces left. The average number of Aces ought to be $(20/52) \times 4 = 1.53$, which happens to be impossible to attain. Since once again the number of Aces is about double the average number, we add a correction of 4 per cent.

Suppose 20 cards remained and there were four Aces left. Then, compared with the average number of Aces, 1.53, there are 4/1.53 or about 2.6 times the average amount. If there were 2.0 times the average amount, we should add a correction of $(2.0 - 1.0) \times 4$ or 4 per cent. If there were 3.0 times the average amount, we should add a correction of $(3.0 - 1.0) \times 4$ or 8 per cent. With 2.6

* The idea is explained in elementary trigonometry books and also in books of mathematical tables. It is simple and requires no understanding of mathematics.

times the average amount, we should add a correction of $(2.6 - 1.0) \times 4$ or 6.4 per cent. The general formula for the correction due to Ace-richness or Ace-poorness is: $[13A/N - 1] \times 4$ where A is the number of as yet unseen Aces and N is the total number of as yet unseen cards. A negative figure means the deck is Ace-poor and the player's advantage will be reduced (perhaps even eliminated altogether) by the negative correction.

Because the additional calculations involved here, when added to the work of playing the Tens strategy, will prove overburdening to most players, I recommend that the reader who is counting Aces as well as Tens at first merely "lean in the indicated direction," rather than making a precise calculation.

In actual play, because of early habits I formed, I do not use the formula in a memorized way. Rather, I do the following equivalent mental steps. First, I estimate the normal number of Aces by computing N/13. Then I divide A, the actual number of Aces remaining, by N/13 getting 13 A/N. This is the number actually present, expressed in terms of the normal number. Then I subtract one from this figure and multiply by 4. It seems tedious at first glance but I have found that with practice it becomes natural, quick, and effortless.

The Remarkable Gain from Proper "End Play"

A few years ago, a now legendary figure, sometimes described as "the little dark-haired guy from Southern California" (we purposely avoid giving his name) approached a large and famous casino in Reno. The story goes that he explained that he would like to play for large stakes—the house limit or more, if possible—and that he wanted a private game without publicity because he had tax problems. He set down carefully stipulated conditions by which the game would be played that probably did not deviate from the spirit of the game. As a bachelor "steadily earning five figures," he had accumulated appreciable capital and was able, no doubt, to convince the casino that he had considerably more still. The house, thinking it had its usual advantage, was probably more than happy to accept these conditions.

Although I do not know the details of the proposition, it is not hard to make a reasonable guess as to what they were. From what I have learned through the grapevine, it seems likely that what I call end-play (to be described below) was the main ingredient of this particular coup. If so, the conditions for the game would be as follows. The casino's usual rules, as to drawing and standing, doubling down, splitting, and insurance, are to be in force. In addition, the player may *vary,* at will from deal to deal, both the number of hands he takes and the amounts he bets. Furthermore, the casino will deal down to the last card before shuffling. At first sight, this set of conditions seems pretty harmless. But, before we see what *happened* at the casino in question, let us examine play under these conditions more closely.

Imagine, first, that seven cards, all Aces and Tens, remain to be played. What happens if you decide to take exactly three hands? Then when you pick up your three hands you find each one consists of either (*A,A*), (*A,10*), or (*10,10*). The dealer, however, receives only one Ace or one Ten, and since the deck runs out, he must shuffle before getting his next card. You now have three powerful hands facing him and, besides, he must draw his next card from a deck that is poor in Aces and Tens. Generally, all three of your hands win. It is not hard to see the principle behind this: count Aces and Tens and, when the end of the deck gets rich in Aces and Tens, take just enough hands so that the dealer only gets one of these cards and must shuffle to get his other card. The advantages frequently range from

10 to 100 per cent in these situations. Money is won at a truly dizzying rate.

An alternate variation goes as follows. Suppose there are five cards left, mostly Aces and Tens, and that you decide to take five hands. Then you get all five of the cards in this favored group, and the dealer gets none of them for he runs out of cards and must shuffle before dealing the first card to himself. If you now get a Ten as your first card this gives you a 15 to 20 per cent advantage; starting with an Ace gives you a 35 to 40 per cent advantage.

Ironically, on the other hand, if it happens that the end of the deck is very poor in Aces and Tens, this too can be turned to advantage. Suppose, for example, that there are twelve small cards left. The player should take, say, five hands and place very small bets on each. Now all twelve cards are used up in dealing the hands and, since mostly small cards are involved, some cards will certainly be drawn, forcing a shuffle. When the deck is shuffled, twelve small cards are missing and therefore the new cards will be dealt from a residue whose ratio is 24/16 or 1.5. A few cards will be drawn but, although it fluctuates in individual situations, on the average the ratio will also be 1.5 at the end of the round. Thus, by taking five hands to keep the small cards on the table during the shuffle, the player has created a series of highly favorable situations.

We now return to the story that happened at the casino. The little dark-haired guy is said to have played for several successive nights. The first night he won ten or fifteen thousand dollars. Then, on successive nights he lost and won similar amounts. When the casino became accustomed to these large surges and when it was clear that they were primed to hang on even though they were well behind, he began playing to win. Hour after hour the money piled up. It is told that somewhere between $40,000 and $86,000, the casino "snapped" and called off the game. The latter figure is supposed to be the authentic one, but there are varying reports. This is probably a result of the fact that there were reportedly but four witnesses to the game—the player and three casino people. This idea of no publicity paid handsomely. During the next two years, the little dark-haired guy visited many other Nevada casinos. As an unusually convincing talker, he sold many of them his proposition. He was finally barred throughout the state, but not before he had won more than $250,000. This man now lives in a mansion in southern California, still a bachelor of sorts. He augments his kitty with his $25,000 (?) salary as an employee of a certain California space-age corporation and by steady winnings at the track.

Of course, since nearly every casino in Nevada now refuses to allow end play, the method is nearly dead. Many casinos are so intimidated that they will not set up private games. But keep it in mind, just in case.

6

The System Is Tested in Nevada

I thought that the strategy based on counting Fives might make an interesting paper at an upcoming Annual Meeting of the American Mathematical Society in Washington, D. C. I planned to fly down from the Massachusetts Institute of Technology, where I was then teaching and where I made my blackjack computer calculations. A few days before the meeting, the society, as is customary, published abstracts of the two hundred or so talks that were to be given. Included was my abstract describing the Fives strategy, "Fortune's Formula: A Winning Strategy for Blackjack" [39].

Two evenings before I left for the meeting, I was surprised by a call from Dick Stewart of the Boston Globe inquiring about the abstract. The paper sent a photographer out to take my picture; meanwhile, I explained the basic ideas of my system to Mr. Stewart over the telephone.

The next morning I was amazed to see a picture of myself with a story on the front page of the Boston Globe [4]. Within hours, the story and more pictures were released across the country by the news services to their thousands of subscribing newspapers [6, 19, 24, 27, 28, 33, 43].

Following my paper in Washington, I was forced to give a press conference. After this I was televised by a major network and interviewed on a number of radio programs. When I returned to my office at the Massachusetts Institute of Technology, my desk was heaped with mail and phone messages, spurred by the continuing publicity [27, 35, 37].

During the next weeks hundreds of letters and long distance phone calls rained in, the bulk of which were requests for copies of my paper and any further available information. Interspersed among this correspondence were a considerable number of offers to back me in a casino test of my system. The amounts proffered ranged from a few thousand dollars to as much as $100,000! Together they totalled a quarter of a million dollars.

Carefully, I screened the offers. I rejected an offer if the person or persons putting up the money could not prove that they could afford to lose their total investment. The reason, of course, is that there is some small risk of a very bad streak, even with winning strategies, as we discussed earlier. I was also worried about the possibilities of being cheated.

Since the $100,000 was the most attractive, I considered it first. It was offered jointly by two New York multimillionaires, whom I shall refer to as Mr. X and Mr. Y. They are both large-scale gamblers. Mr. Y once lost $100,000 in one of the casino games without being seriously hurt financially. Mr. X's gambling activities involve hundreds of thousands of dollars and even millions in profits; he has been famous for years in gambling circles from Miami to Las Vegas. I later learned both that he was familiar with the exploits of "the little dark-haired guy" (Chapter 5) and that he had made large sums himself at blackjack. Thus he was thoroughly "sold" in advance.

Preparations.

When I told Mr. X of my interest, he drove up from New York one Sunday. He showed me enough of his practical gambling knowledge and card skill to persuade me that he could quickly detect cheating. At the invitation and expense of Mr. X and Mr. Y., I flew from Boston to New York several times to discuss the system and to plan a trip to Nevada.

There were two main approaches that we could adopt for betting. One, which I shall term "wild," involves betting the casino limit whenever the advantage to the player exceeds some small figure, say 1 per cent. This method produces, on the average, the greatest gain in the shortest time. However, in a short run of a few days, the fluctuations in the player's total capital generally are violent and a large bankroll is required. Mr. X and Mr. Y said that they would back this to the extent of $100,000 and that they would go farther if necessary.

The $10,000 Bankroll

I was not in favor of the wild approach since there were too many things I did not know about the gambling world. I also had no idea how I or my backers would react if I were to get behind, say, $50,000. Furthermore, the purpose of the trip from my point of view was to test my system rather than to make big money for Mr. X and Mr. Y. I thus preferred being certain of a moderate win, rather than a probable, but somewhat uncertain, big win. I therefore favored another approach, which I shall call "conservative" play. This involves betting twice the amount of the minimum bet when the advantage is 1 per cent, four times the minimum when the advantage is 2 per cent, and finally levelling off at ten times the minimum when the advantage is 5 per cent or more in the player's favor. I determined that if my bets would range from $50 to $500 (the highest casino maximum generally available), then $6,000 or $7,000 would probably be adequate capital. To be safe, we took along $10,000—a hundred one-hundred dollar bills.

When the M. I. T. one-week spring recess came, Mr. X. and I flew on a Thursday evening to Reno where Mr. Y. was to join us later. We checked into one of the large Reno Hotels about 2 A.M. and immediately went to sleep. Early the next morning we began investigating casinos.

The Warmup

Our plan, insisted upon by me, was to proceed with caution: we would start "small," betting $1 to $10 and would gradually increase the amount of the bets as I gained experience. Eventually we planned to bet $50 to $500. I planned to use the Tens system as it seemed to give a wider range of opportunity than the Fives system and with only a modest increase in the amount of memorizing.

First we drove to a casino outside of town. In an hour or so of play I won a few dollars and then when the establishment closed for three hours because of Good Friday, we returned to Reno. During the evening we investigated a number of casinos to determine which had rules that were most favorable. As the best spot for practicing, we selected a casino that dealt down to the last card and allowed the player to double down on any hand, split any pair, and insure. This set of rules is more favorable than is ordinarily found.

After a sumptuous dinner and a rest, I returned alone to the casino we had chosen. It was then about 10 P.M. Mr. X did not accompany me because he is well known to that casino's owner and we did not wish to attract attention. I began by alternately playing for fifteen or twenty minutes at a time and then resting for a few minutes. Whenever I would sit down again I would always choose the table with the fewest players. My behavior pattern—I paused for thought and stared at all the cards played—made it apparent that I was using some "system." But system players are frequent, if not common, in the casinos. In fact, they are welcome as long as they are losing and gradually I fell farther behind until, by 5 A.M., I was down $100.

At this time, business fell off sharply and I was finally able to get a table completely to myself. My new dealer was particularly unfriendly. When I asked to be dealt two hands, she refused, saying that it was house policy that I must bet $2 per hand to play two hands. Since this change in the scale of betting would confuse my records of the evening's play, I refused. Besides, I was getting tired and irritable.

I pointed out to this dealer that at least eight other dealers had let me play two hands without complaint and therefore it could hardly be a house policy. She said that the reason was to keep other players from being crowded out. However, I remarked that there were no other players at my table so her reason did not seem to apply. She became angry at this and dealt as rapidly as she could.

A few hands later, the ratio of others/Tens dropped to 2.0, a 1 per cent advantage for me. Being thoroughly annoyed by now, I broke my self-imposed discipline. I advanced to the $2 to $20 scale and bet $4. I won and the ratio advanced to 1.7, a 2 per cent advantage. I let my $8 ride and won again. The ratio obligingly dropped to 1.5, a 4 per cent advantage. I let my $16 ride and won again. I left $20 of this $32 on the table with the remark that it was time for me to take a small profit. The ratio fluctuated between 1.4 and 1.0 and I continued to make $20 bets. By the time we came to the end of the deck, I had recouped my $100 loss and had a few dollars profit besides.

As I picked up my winnings and left, I noticed an odd mixture of anger and awe on the dealer's face. It was as though she had peeked for a brief moment through a familiar door into a familiar room and, maybe, she had glimpsed something strange and impossible.

This training session brought mixed blessings. I would regret my rash behavior in a few days, for the casino's operators took special notice of me. On the other hand, my attention was drawn to the doubling-up betting pattern that I had used in the last few minutes; it consisted of betting 1 unit, winning and letting the 2 units ride, winning and letting the 4 units ride, etc. This pattern of play resembles the well-known doubling-up system, or (small) Martingale, which is widely used in almost every gambling game. The pattern I used above is not sensible for those gambling games in which the house has the advantage; but in blackjack, with the player's use of counting methods, it is as profitable as any other way of putting down money *at favorable times*. Furthermore, since this system is so widely and so unsuccessfully practiced, it makes an excellent disguise for the counting player. Also, in blackjack there often seem to be favorable runs wherein the advantages (e.g., 1,2,4 percent) fit (Table 5.2) the doubling-up scheme well. (e.g., 2,4,8 units) If the advantages come somewhere near these figures, I think it pays to slightly shade or increase the bets, if necessary, to continue the camouflage of a doubling-up sequence. Also, the casual touch of leaving your chips untouched between hands seems nice.

A Hundred Here, a Thousand There

Sandy-eyed and stiff, I woke up early Saturday afternoon, had an elaborate breakfast. Afterwards, Mr. X and I again visited the casino outside town. Within minutes, by playing the $10 to $100 scale, I won $200 or $300. Mr. X joined me and we played for a couple of hours. We accumulated $650, and the house began to shuffle the deck several cards before the end. Since the favorable situations arise with greatest frequency at the end of the deck, shuffling-up can sharply reduce the rate of profit. Because we were only practicing, it seemed discreet for us to leave now and hope that we could come back later for a few full-scale hours.

Mr. X and I were still expecting Mr. Y in Reno. On Saturday evening Mr. Y arrived. After dinner, Mr. Y and I set out to seek our fortune. We first visited one of the most famous clubs, an enormous building in the center of downtown Reno, and we began to play at the $500 maximum tables. (The maximum generally ranges from $100 to $500 in Nevada, varying from casino to casino and frequently from table to table within a given casino. With our capital, we preferred the highest maximum possible.) In only fifteen minutes we won $500, warming up at a $25 to $250 scale. Our dealer decided to alert the management of the casino. She pressed a concealed button under the table with her foot. Within minutes the owner and his son arrived. There were pleasantries and politenesses exchanged but they made their point: the deck would be shuffled as often as necessary to prevent us from winning.

Most casino owners had learned, over the last decade, that some players would wait until very special combinations of cards would arise, near the end of the deck and that then they would sharply up their bet, sometimes going from $1 to $500. These players were stopped by always shuffling the deck five or ten cards from the end.

Therefore, to be safe, the owners instructed our dealer to shuffle no later than 12 to 15 cards from the end. Fortunately for them, they waited to see the results. We were not planning any ulterior moves; we continued to use the same Tens strategy that we had used all evening. This strategy locates favorable situations after the first hand has been played, even if only four cards have been dealt.

A few minor, yet favorable, situations appeared and were exploited by us. Thereupon the deck was shuffled 25 cards from the end. Still, occasional minor favorable situations arose. Finally the dealer began shuffling 42 cards from the end, that is, after only two hands had been played! This fencing took twenty minutes, or so, and by that time a combination of bad luck, the club's unfavorable rules, and the shuffling allowed us to squeeze out only an additional $80. It seemed useless to continue playing at this casino, so we stopped.

We then visited a casino in one of the large hotels. We had been told that they used a "cheat" dealer on "big-money" players. After being cheated on the very first hand, in an incident described in detail in the chapter on cheating, we moved on.

Nine-Hundred Dollars Bet on a Single Hand

In the next casino, the maximum was only $300 but this limit was compensated for by excellent rules: the player could insure, split any pair, and double down on any set of cards. We purchased $2000 in chips from the cashier and selected a table at which there were no other players. I lost steadily and, at the end of four hours of play, I was almost $1700 behind. I was quite discouraged. However, I followed the pattern of countless hapless players before me (with, I hope, better reason) and decided to wait for the deck to become favorable "just once more" so I could recoup some of my losses.

In a few minutes the deck obliged, suddenly producing a ratio of others/Tens of 1.4, a 5 per cent advantage, which called for the maximum bet of $300. Curiously, my remaining chips amounted to precisely $300. As I tried to decide whether to quit if I lost this one, I picked up my hand and found a pair of Eights. They had to be split. I flung three one-hundred dollar bills from my wallet onto the second

Eight. On one of the Eights I was dealt a Three. I had to double down so I flung three more one-hundred dollar bills onto this hand. Nine-hundred dollars were now lying on the table—the largest bet I had yet made.

The dealer was showing a Six up and turned out to have a Ten under. He promptly busted. Now I was only eight-hundred dollars down. This deck continued to be favorable and the next "went" favorable after the first hand. In a few minutes I wiped out all my losses and went ahead $255. With this burst of good fortune, Mr. Y and I decided to quit for the evening.

Again the Tens system had shown a feature that would appear repeatedly: moderately heavy losing streaks, mixed with "lucky streaks" of the most dazzling brilliance.

The next afternoon Mr. X, Mr. Y, and I visited the casino outside town again. Before sitting down to play, I made a phone call. When I came back my friends told me the casino had barred us from play, but that they would be only too happy to pick up our meal tab. I called over the floor manager, and asked him what this was all about. He explained, in a very friendly and courteous manner, that the staff had seen me playing the day before and that they were very puzzled by my steady winning at a rate that was large for my bet sizes. He said also that they could not figure out what was going on, but that they had finally decided, in the light of their previous experience, that a card-counting system was involved. My technique was becoming hard to detect.

Evidently they were discouraged when they estimated the power of the system that faced them, for the floor manager said that the owner had deliberated at length before deciding to bar us. The casino, he said, had fearlessly played against all card counters—and he reeled off a series of names that meant nothing to me—and had beaten them all, with one exception. He described the only player that had been previously barred as "a little dark-haired guy from Southern California." We have already mentioned the techniques of this individual on pages 94-97 and will say more about him and other famous early players later on.

We returned to our hotel and, while my friends took care of business for a couple of hours, I passed the time away by betting $5 to $50 at the blackjack tables. Despite the annoying presence of a shill, I won about $550. At this point, the pit boss asked me to stop playing at the hotel and to tell the same to Messrs. X and Y and any other friends I might have. He did say, however, that we could enjoy unlimited free drinks on the house. Immediately I had a Moscow mule and then went to tell my friends that they had been banned from this casino without their ever having played there.

It was almost suppertime Sunday when the three of us revisited the casino at which I had made the $900 bet. I was warmly remembered as the rich playboy of the night before who had been down $1700 before wriggling off the hook by some quirk of fate. We were invited to dine, courtesy of the house, as a prelude to the evening's gaming festivities. After two $4 entrees of assorted baked oysters on the half shell and various supporting dishes, capped with wine, I set out somewhat unsteadily for the gaming tables: I was truly a lamb readied for the slaughter. Within a few minutes, however, I was at peak alertness. After four hours of betting $25 to $300, I was ahead $2000. Since I was beginning to tire, with the utmost reluctance, I decided to return to my hotel.

I remember that casino fondly: the courtesy and hospitality, the spacious, attractive modern dining room with its fine cuisine, and the casino with its juicy little clusters of blackjack tables, the favorable rules, and, last but not least, the free money.

The Twenty-Five Dollar Minimum Game

My friends and I were again ready for action (action both in the customary sense and in the mathematical sense of the sum total of all bets made) early Monday afternoon. We drove to the south end (Stateline) of Lake Tahoe. About 6 P.M. we arrived at a large, brightly lighted gambling factory. It was jammed. I was barely able to get a seat at the blackjack tables.

A few minutes after I placed on the table the $2000 worth of chips I had purchased from the cashier, a pit boss rushed over to invite me to dinner and the show. I, in turn, requested (with success) that my two friends be included. I began a game and within a few minutes—as I began to win—Mr. X joined me. In forty minutes, I won $1300 and Mr. X, who was betting wildly, won $2000. Then we took time out for our free dinner, which featured filet mignon and champagne. Within hours, destiny would present us with a bill for our "free" dinner. The charge? Eleven-*thousand* dollars!

After dinner we strolled over to another casino in which there were both the $500 limit and acceptable rules. As usual, I purchased $2000 in chips from the cashier and selected the least busy table. From the beginning I was plagued by $1 bettors who came and went, generally slowing down the game, who concealed cards so that they were hard to count, and who created many other small annoyances.

Whenever a small bettor arrived at the table I pointedly reduced my minimum bet from $50 to $1. After a few minutes the pit boss "got the message" and asked me if I would like a private table. When I said it would "transport me with ecstasy," he explained that, in general, the club did not like the psychological effect of a private table on the other customers. However, with a trace of a smile, he said that a $25 minimum game could be arranged, and wondered if that would be satisfactory. I promptly agreed and a sign to that effect was installed which cleared the table of all customers but me. A small crowd gathered to watch quietly their somewhat plumpish fellow lamb go to the slaughter.

Seventeen-Thousand Dollars in Two Hours

After I had won a few hundred dollars, the pit boss was amazed and delighted to see another "well-heeled" lamb wander up and sit down at my table; it was none other than my friend Mr. X who thereupon "jumped in" the game. I then took the responsibility, for both of us, for keeping the count and calling the signals. Within thirty minutes we had emptied the table's money tray—the blackjack version of "breaking the bank." The once-smiling pit boss trembled with fear.

Other employees began to panic. One of our dealers bleated to her boyfriend higher-up, "Oh, help me. Please. Help me." The pit boss was trying to explain away our win to a nervous knot of subordinates. While the money tray was being restocked, the crowd swelled. They began to cheer their David on against the casino Goliath.

One bystander blurted out rather loudly that he had seen us off to a roaring start in Reno two nights earlier and wondered if we had done there what we were now doing here. As the pit boss listened attentively, we quickly hushed up the bystander with tales of woe.

In two hours, we broke the bank again. The great heaps of chips in front of us included more than $17,000 in profits. I had won about $6,000 and Mr. X, betting wildly, had won $11,000. I was tiring rapidly. The after effects of our huge dinner, the increased effort in managing two hands, and the strain of the last few days were telling. I began to find it very difficult to count properly and observed Mr. X was equally far gone. I insisted that we quit and I cashed in my $6,000. As I did so, I was startled to find three or four pretty girls wandering back and forth across my path smiling affectionately.

After wending my Ulyssian way back to the tables, I watched horror stricken as Mr. X, having refused to stop playing, poured back thousands. In the forty-five minutes that it took to persuade him to leave, it cost the two of us about $11,000 of our $17,000. Even so, when we returned to our hotel that evening we were ahead $13,000 so far on the trip.

On Tuesday we paid a series of visits to a downtown club that had bad rules and shuffled five to ten cards from the end. We gradually but steadily lost about $2000, playing $50 to $500. The player could double down on 10 and 11 only, could not insure, and the dealer hit soft 17. As will be seen in the chapter on rules variations, the player is whittled down at an average rate of slightly less than one per cent while awaiting favorable situations. When these situations do arise, they are reduced somewhat in both frequency and favorability. Playing $50 to $500, the Tens strategy produces perhaps $500 per hour* with favorable rules and about $400 per hour with typical rules.† With the unfavorable rules just described, the strategy probably produces about $250 per hour and the risk of bad fluctuations rises sharply.†

This situation has led me to develop a much more powerful strategy than the Tens strategy to deal specifically with the more unfavorable casinos. That strategy, sketched in Chapter 9, allows the player to count *all* the cards and locates nearly every favorable situation. It is more difficult than the Tens strategy, but not prohibitively so. I have called it the "ultimate" strategy because, in the very early and middle parts of the deck, it is very close to the best possible

* Assuming 100 hands per hour.

† These estimates are conservative. Records of tens of thousands of hands suggest the true-win rates are double these.

strategy that can ever be devised. A truly perfect strategy would require a high-speed computer specifically working out the details of each and every hand as it arises, based on the cards that have been seen so far.

My friends and I recalled that the club in which I first practiced so lengthily had excellent rules and made a practice of dealing down to the last card in the deck. We decided to pay it a return visit. Mr. Y and I purchased $1,000 in chips and began to play. We immediately began to win, but within minutes the owner was on the scene. In a panic, he gave the dealer and the pit boss instructions.

Then an amazing sequence began. Whenever I changed my bet size, the dealer shuffled. Whenever I varied the number of hands I took (by this time I could play from one to eight hands at one time and faster than the best dealers could deal), the dealer shuffled. The dealer against whom I had played last in my practice session was standing in the background (had she "fingered" me?) saying over and over in reverent tones how much I had advanced in skill since the other night. Finally I happened to scratch my nose and the dealer shuffled! Incredulous! I asked her whether she would shuffle each time I scratched my nose. She said she would. A few more scratches convinced me she meant what she said. I asked whether any change in my behavior pattern, no matter how minute, would cause her to shuffle. She said it would.

I was now playing merely even with the house, as the shuffling destroyed nearly all my advantage (except that gained from seeing the burned card). But, by chance I moved ahead about three hundred dollars. I then asked for some larger denomination chips—$50 or $100—as all I had were twenties. The owner stepped forward and said that the house would not sell them to us. He then had a new deck brought in and carefully spread, first face down, then face up. Curious, I asked why they spread them face down. Although the practice is a common one in the casinos, seldom do they examine the backs of the cards for a couple of minutes, as these people were doing. The dealer explained that it was believed that I had unusually acute vision (I wear glasses) and could distinguish tiny blemishes on the back of the cards. This, they surmised, is what enabled me to foretell what cards were going to be dealt. I scoffed but the house, still panicky as my wins continued, brought in four new decks in five minutes.

After disposing of that particular house theory, I pressed them to tell us what they thought about my "secret." The dealer claimed, then, that I could count every card as it was played, and that therefore I knew exactly which cards had not yet been played at each and every instant. Now it is a well-known fact to students of mnemotechny (the science of memory training) that one can readily learn to memorize in proper order part or all of a deck of cards as it is dealt out. However, I am familiar enough with the method involved [12] to know that the information, when so memorized, cannot be used quickly enough for play in blackjack. So I challenged the dealer by rashly claiming that no one in the world could watch 35 cards dealt quickly off a pack and then tell me quickly how many of each type of card remained.

She answered by claiming that the pit boss, next to her, could do just that. I told them I would pay $5 on the spot for a demonstration. They both looked down sheepishly and would not answer. I made my offer $50. They remained silent and ashamed. Then my friend Mr. Y increased the offer to $500. There was no response from these "sportsmen." We left in disgust.

At the next club that Mr. Y and I visited, the blackjack tables were packed, so we inquired about a private game. A balding, effeminate man scampered out and, in nervous high tones, told us that he knew what we were up to and they were on to us and "no thank you." Another sportsman!

Since I had proved the system and the millionaires had business elsewhere, we agreed to terminate our little gambling experiment. In 30 man-hours of medium and large-scale play, we had built $10,000 into $21,000. At no point did we have to go into our original capital more than $1300 (plus expenses). Our experiment was a success and my system performed in practice just as the theory on which it is based predicted it would.

Inasmuch as we had an hour to kill before leaving for the airport, we visited a friend of Mr. X at a casino the friend operated. I was in favor of having a last big round of play but Mr. X did not want his friend "hurt." Rapidly bored by the conversation, I wandered to the blackjack tables. I found three silver dollars in my pocket, inflicted on me as change by the last local merchant I had patronized. I decided to dispose of the silver dollars at the table. Soon a great doubling up sequence of favorable situations came and, in five minutes, my $3 became $35. Mr. X's friend never knew that a word from Mr. X had saved him more than $1000 in that few minutes.

My trip to Nevada gives an ironic twist to the words of a casino operator who was being interviewed on a national television program. When he was asked whether the customers in Nevada ever walked away winners, he said, "When a lamb goes to the slaughter, the lamb *might* kill the butcher. But *we* always bet on the butcher."

The day of the lamb had come.

7

How to Spot Cheating

Before I became seriously interested in blackjack, I, and everyone that I knew, was convinced that, although blackjack dealers in casinos were often fantastically skillful with cards and could cheat if they so desired, they did not cheat. The well-publicized argument is that the casinos enjoy a natural advantage in the game and will win anyhow. Why should a casino risk possible exposure with its resultant bad publicity, loss of customers, and perhaps even loss of their gaming license? Alternatively, why would a crooked dealer, working for an honest casino, risk loss of his job in order to line his pockets?

We might answer this with another question, "Isn't there widespread corruption in political life and in the business world?" And also, isn't it often for the same stakes (money) and with comparable risks (loss of position or of license to operate, bad publicity, etc.)? Why then should legalized gambling be more immune from dishonesty than "legalized" politics or "legalized" business?

Since I was originally naive enough to swallow the widely publicized argument that blackjack as played in the casinos is generally honest, it took painful personal experience to convince me of the contrary. The first such experience was not long in coming.

The Knockout Dealer: A Stubborn Expert Wastes $20,000 in a Single Night

One afternoon during the test of the system in Nevada, which is described in Chapter 6, Mr. X went off alone to play the Tens Strategy. Early the next morning he told me that he had been playing steadily for eight to ten hours at one of the large hotels. He was making house-limit bets of $500 in sufficiently favorable situations. After a few hours he won $13,000. At this point the hotel brought in its "knockout" dealer—a cheat employed specifically for disposing of big winners.

Her method of cheating was to peek at the top card when it came time for her to draw to her own hand. If she liked the top card, she dealt it (honestly) to herself. If she did not like it, she dealt herself the card just below the top card, commonly referred to as the "second." Even though she did not know what the second was, it was a better risk than the top card about half the time.

Mr. X stubbornly played on, hoping he could beat the cheat anyhow. The cheat faced him for forty minutes at a time. Then she rested for twenty minutes during which time the game was honest again. Mr. X hoped to win more in the twenty-minute sessions than he would be cheated out of in the forty-minute sessions. But he made a fatal error. He continued to bet on a large scale against the knockout dealer, rather than reducing his bets to a few dollars and waiting until she had to be relieved. Thus he lost too heavily against her. After a few hours he had lost back $20,000, cancelling his $13,000 lead and putting him $7,000 in the hole. When Mr. X complained to the owner, a person who has been instrumental in the operation of several large casinos, the owner explained that a (mythical?) Texan had won $17,000 the day before and the casino could not afford further losses.

The Queen of Hearts

Anxious to learn to protect myself from being cheated, I visited this particular casino the next afternoon, accompanied by Mr. Y. Mr. X had described the knockout dealer to us: a thinnish, grim-faced woman of about forty, with black hair which was beginning to gray.

I purchased $1000 worth of chips from the cashier and seated myself at the nearest table. I bet $30 and then the dealer dealt a card to me, and one to herself. As she dealt the second card to me, the pit boss rushed over, stopped her, took back the cards, and called over a dealer to replace her. The new dealer was a thinnish, grim-faced woman of about forty, with black hair which was beginning to turn gray.

I received a pair of Eights and the dealer had a Three showing. I split my Eights and got totals of 20 and 18. The dealer's hole card was a Ten. Mr. Y and I watched as the dealer, holding the deck edge-up, bent the top card back slightly to see what it was. We saw it too: the Queen of Hearts. That would have busted her so she dealt the second card to herself. It was an Eight, giving her 21, and she raked in our $60. Angrily Mr. Y spelled out for her what she had done. She reddened and looked down. She said nothing and pretended not to hear our loud, angry protests. When the pit boss came over, he also showed no reaction. There was nothing we could do—"it was our word against theirs." We left, poorer but wiser.

After that experience and before writing this chapter, I went on several exploratory trips with the purpose of investigating cheating. I played at most of the major casinos in Las Vegas and Reno for periods ranging from a few minutes (cheating) to several hours, with bets ranging from $1 to $50. I was cheated frequently enough to learn to classify and spot a dozen or so current techniques. There was cheating at large plush casinos, as well as at smaller out-of-the-way places. There was cheating at all betting levels, even for 25¢!! In many additional instances, the cards behaved so strangely that I suspected cheating although I could not actually see seconds being dealt (with a good dealer it is extremely difficult to see).

On both the Reno-Tahoe trip and the first Las Vegas trip (taken four months after the Reno-Tahoe trip), I had the good fortune to be accompanied by individuals who were able to play the Ten-count strategy, who were expert both at demonstrating and spotting dealer-cheating at the game, and who patiently instructed me in the ways that the dealer can cheat. Furthermore, since each of these individuals had money invested in the play, they were always at my side, watching attentively.

I emphasize that the cheating incidents described are my personal experiences. I do not wish to imply that they are necessarily representative. The average amount of cheating might be far greater or it might be virtually nonexistent. In addition, it probably varies with such things as changes in government, casino management and ownership, and the size of bets, the time of day, and the individual dealer.

In some cases, an honest casino might unknowingly hire a dishonest dealer. This dealer could cheat the house by letting a friend win heavily. If the house checks receipts regularly, they might notice that the given dealer frequently has unusually poor shifts. In order to prevent detection, a logical cover-up by the dealer is to cheat other players to make up the deficit. Some people describe this behavior of the dealer as a Robin-Hood function.

I emphatically do not wish to imply that one part of Nevada is more or less free from cheating than any other part. I also believe that, at the time of this writing, the cheating problem is not great enough so that people should completely refrain from playing. However, anyone who does play blackjack should learn without delay some of the elementary ways in which his opponent can cheat. (Sad to say, this advice applies equally to the other card games, both casino and private).

I have been told by a very reliable source that, in the first five years of the Nevada Gaming Control Board's operation, they have closed down more than twenty casinos for cheating [42]. Little, if any, publicity is generally given to these proceedings, and the casinos usually reopen promptly under new management. However, the Gaming Control Board seems to be the Nevada blackjack player's only source of appeal after being cheated. If you have a complaint, I suggest that you telephone or visit the Board offices in Carson City or Las Vegas as promptly as possible—preferably no later than twenty-four hours after the incident has occurred. Then swear out a written complaint and send it to the Nevada Gaming Control Board by *registered mail.* Keep *two* carbon copies for yourself. Even though you may be angry, it is important that you be as factual and objective as you can, in both your verbal and written reports. They will have much greater weight that way. You should describe the incident in much the same manner as you would a traffic accident. Try to include the date and time, the name of the casino, the names and/or description of the casino employees involved, a detailed description of the cheating itself, and any witnesses you can find to corroborate any or all of your statements. This is a rather tough bill of goods for the uninitiated player to suddenly think up all by himself; thus the Gaming Control Board probably hears about only a small fraction of the cheating that players notice. The amount of cheating varies from almost none to over 90 per cent, depending in which area of the world you are playing. There is a similar variation in the amount of help the authorities will give a player who has been cheated, varying from no help at all to a great deal. You may wish to investigate in detail the conditions in your area before you play.

There are dozens of ways to cheat at blackjack and at card games in general. All we can do here is sketch some of the more popular ones, based on my experience with the casinos. I have found that an understanding of the facts that I shall give here provides adequate protection for the player in the great majority of situations that come up.

Marked Cards

One main technique in cheating is for the dealer to identify the top card in order to deal a second, if it is advantageous, at some appropriate point in the game. The simplest way of identifying a card from its back is to mark on the back, in some kind of code, just what the card is. A marked deck is called "paper." Millions of decks of marked cards are produced annually and are readily purchased by mail from supply houses specializing in crooked gambling equipment. They are also available in most "magic" stores.

All the most widely used standard brands are available. There is no safety in the fact that a pack may have been manufactured by a reputable company; someone else can easily "mark" the deck. For example, anyone can purchase at nominal cost special inks and brushes for this purpose. For the details of how cards are marked, pictures of marked cards, and some of the styles of marking, the reader is referred to [13, 17, 22, 31, 38]. Photographs of second-dealing (discussed below), also appear in most of these references.

On one occasion I was betting from $2 to $20 while a card-expert stood by to protect me against possible cheating. A short while after I began to play, the deck was taken out and a new one was brought in. I requested the old deck ostensibly as a souvenir but in reality I wanted it in order to check for markings. Even though I insisted on that particular deck, the casino refused to give it to me, and instead, after much hunting and digging, produced another deck. The latter was in considerably better condition than the one they had refused to give up. Suspicious, I continued to play against the new deck and, as I was winning moderately—there was a tremendous streak of favorable situations—my suspicions were lulled. After about thirty minutes I stopped and my friend told me that I was playing against a marked deck. He said that both of the dealers against whom I played dealt seconds whenever called for if the bets were $10 or more, and not otherwise. Immediately an odd incident came to mind. Once a card stuck in the deck, held only by its corner. It did not come loose until the dealer flicked his wrist sharply. The card must have been a second, for it was hanging there and was held both above and below by other cards in the deck.

My friend said he did not pull me out of the game because I was winning anyhow. Although I did win something, my winnings were only a small part of what they might have been with such tremendously favorable situations as had occurred.

Frequently dealers of seconds have the habit of "kicking" the wrist of the hand that is holding the deck as part of their motion of dealing. This helps prevent cards from getting stuck and hanging as happened in the above incident. Thus, when you see a dealer who has this otherwise unnecessary motion, it suggests very strongly that he is able to deal seconds.

One of the cheat dealers, who had worked for the casinos on 24-hour call, showed me a novel card-marking method. He took his thumbnail and pressed the backs of Aces and Tens on their top edge. He did not scratch them but rather merely rounded them slightly; when this was done the cards seemed no different than the others in the deck, as I and several friends learned as we hunted for the markings. However, when the deck was held at a certain angle to the light, the edges of the marked cards gleamed just enough so that a trained eye could pick them out. Because of the angles involved in light reflection, when the dealer can see the gleam, no one else can.

This dealer claimed the Gaming Control Board had at different times confiscated several decks which he had so marked and that images of them had been projected, greatly enlarged on a wall, without the markings ever having been detected.

Peeking

Marked cards have the disadvantage that they are concrete evidence that can be used in a court of law. A more common method of identifying the top card, which has the further advantage that it may be used with any deck whatsoever, is for the dealer to actually look at the face of the top card. This method is often referred to as peeking.

A skilled dealer can peek at the top card in plain view of a table full of players with almost no risk of being caught. Suppose that a player busts. The dealer collects his chips and his cards. He will often use both hands for this. If he holds the deck in, say, the left hand, as that hand reaches out it is natural to turn it over so the deck is upside down. Try this and freeze your left hand in this partially extended position. Now reach out with your right hand and bend the right rear corner down slightly. Notice that you can identify the card by the exposed part of its face but that this portion of the card is not visible to someone sitting across the table. Now certainly no one is going to reach across with his other hand and bend down the card. But a skilled dealer can accomplish this with the same hand with which he holds the deck, swiftly and invisibly. Fortunately many, if not most, of the cheats seem to be much less practiced at peeking than they are at second dealing so you can, if you are watchful, often catch them as they peek.

If you are ever suspicious, there is one method which will generally either catch the peeking or put a stop to it. It depends on the fact that if the dealer peeks, his eyes must rest upon the card at which he is peeking, unless he uses a "shiner" (to be discussed later). Then while one person plays, another person stands (this has advantages over sitting, as we shall see when we discuss dealing seconds) behind the player and stares at the dealer's eyes. Whenever the dealer's eyes look at the deck, the watcher's eyes flick down to the deck to see if a peek was possible, and then flick back to the dealer's eyes. The watcher should also have his eyes on the deck whenever a card is being dealt.

I have found this technique extremely successful. Some cheat dealers become so tense and nervous about being caught that they become clumsy and are caught all the more quickly. Others stop cheating altogether under the pressure.

A "shiner" is a little concealed mirror which the dealer uses to see the faces of the cards, before or as they are dealt. It might be put in places such as the face of a ring, inside a pipe bowl, or the polished edge of the money tray [31].

A Simple Home Experiment

On granting that the dealer peeks and deals seconds at

will, here is a simple home experiment that will give you an idea of the enormous average advantage he gains on those hands wherein he decides to do this.

Deal out one hand to a single player (imaginary, if necessary), and one to yourself, as dealer. Have the player use, say, the basic strategy. Each time, before you give a card to the player or yourself, peek at the top card. If you prefer not to deal that card, hold it and deal the second card. A certain amount of judgment, as when to deal the top card and when not to, is required here. When you feel your judgment has become good, make an initial bet of one chip on each hand and record the results for one hundred hands. Be sure to shuffle the deck several times each time you need to reshuffle. Most of the time that this experiment is tried it will give a result that is quite favorable for the dealer. Just how favorable the result is can be judged by comparing the results obtained with the typical distribution of results of 100 honest hands as listed in Table 3.10.

To illustrate the idea, I just made a short run of 35 hands. If my own up card was *2* through *6* and if the player requested a card, I dealt him the top card when it was *2* through *7*, and dealt a second instead when the top card was *8* through *A*. However, if my up card was *7* through *A* and if the player requested a card, I dealt him *9*, *10*, or *A*. I held the others, dealing seconds instead. Obvious exceptions were sometimes made in case of doubling down or pair splitting since the player's hole cards were exposed.

The results, *which are not significant because of the small number of hands,* happened to turn out as follows: The house won 28 units, there were three ties, and the player won 11 1/2 units for a net house gain of 17 1/2 units or about 1/2 unit per hand. Forty-two and one-half units were involved on the thirty-five hands because of doubling down, pair-splitting, and naturals.

Dealing Seconds

Dealing seconds is the principle weapon of literally millions of card cheats throughout the world. When competently done, it is almost invisible, even to experts. Sleight of hand and manipulation of cards was already well developed in the sixteenth century. With reference to this, see the report by Gerolamo Cardano [29, pages 132-134], perhaps the most skilled gambler of his day, in which there are stories of the miraculous skill and tricks of Dalmagus (or Dalmautus) and of Francesco Soma.

One of the methods of detection, by listening to the sound of the cards being dealt, is generally useless in the usual noisy casino atmosphere. It is based on the fact that the second, when dealt, rubs other cards on both its surfaces while the top card rubs only on its lower surface. Thus a deal which includes a second generally sounds something like: swish, swish, scrape (second), swish. Of course these sounds, and the difference between them, are apt to be slight, thus it is generally necessary to have quiet to detect this.

To get a very rough idea of the technique of dealing seconds, place a deck of cards in your left hand as though you were about to deal. Now rearrange the deck as follows. The left-front corner should be nestled in the "elbow" or second joint of your index finger. The tip of this finger should be slighty above the top-front edge of the deck (it will keep the third card from being pulled forward by the action of the second). The left-rear corner of the deck should be firmly seated in the palm. The second, third, and fourth fingers should go under the deck and around the right side. Their tips should also be slightly above the top of the deck.

Now, with the thumb, which should be lying comfortably on top of the deck towards the front, pull the top card to the left, say half an inch. This half-an-inch figure is only for illustration as an expert would pull the top card to the left (or *down,* for an important alternate variation) only a very small amount. If your grip is proper, the rest of the deck should have been undisturbed by this motion. The corner of the second card is now exposed. By using your right thumb on that corner, much as in ordinary dealing, slide the second forward and to the right. When it is part way out, grasp it with the thumb and forefinger again just as in ordinary dealing. At about the same time with the *left* thumb, slide the first card back into its original position. If your grip was proper, only the top and second cards were disturbed during the entire process. Proper height of the tips of the second, third, and fourth fingers will prevent the cards below the second from moving when the second card is pulled out. Thus when the deal of the second is complete, the deck appears normal. This is admittedly by no means an expert technique, but it should give you some idea of how second dealing works.

If you used a deck with borders, you may have noticed that, as the second is dealt, the right border* of the top card is almost stationary. However, if a top card is dealt, the right border of the second is partially or totally concealed until the top card has cleared the deck. Thus, one way to spot a second being dealt from a deck with borders is to stare from above the deck at the right border (left border from the player's side of the table) to see whether or not that border moves much as the card is dealt.

To counter this, many second dealers use decks without borders. However, so do a number of honest casinos; thus the mere use of a borderless deck does by no means indicate

* I assume the dealer is right-handed throughout the book. If the dealer is left-handed, the words "right" and "left" should be interchanged by the reader throughout many of these discussions.

cheating. To make it still harder for the player to see a second being dealt, the dealer generally tips the front of the deck up slightly so that the player views the cards edge-on! In this instance the presence or absence of borders is immaterial since the backs of the cards are totally invisible at the instant a card is dealt.

Dealers often tilt the forward end of the deck so far up and back towards their chests that kibitzers who are standing cannot see the back of the top card. In this position anyone can deal a second without being caught. If you try this yourself, simply slide the top card *down* a short distance, deal the second by pulling it forward and up, and restore the top card to its initial position.

Perhaps the most popular type of borderless cards now in use in the casinos are the famous Bee No. 67. The pattern on the backs consists of solid diamonds separated by broken diagonal white stripes. This pattern seems to dazzle or blind the untrained eye; its use seems to increase the difficulties in the detection of seconds. When the wrist flick is employed this pattern is even more effective in blinding the eye to the dealing of a second.

Deck Stacking: The High-Low Pickup

During my exploration of casinos to study the cheating methods actually employed, I came across a novel sort of game. The rules were pretty standard except that the game was played with four decks all shuffled together. Further, the cards were dealt from a "shoe." This was a black plastic box, which was open at the top. The four decks were shuffled, and then placed in the box with their long edges down. There was a slit in the end of the box at the bottom and a small oval hole running up from the slit for a short distance. The backs of the cards showed through the oval. The dealer placed his right thumb through the oval, and, to deal the cards, drew them down and out through the slit, one by one.

This seemed like an ideal game with which to use the Ten-count strategy because, with so many cards in play, the fluctuations in favorability from hand to hand (which result from cards played on the previous hand) would be much smaller than in the one deck game. Thus when large bets were being placed, there would be much less fluctuation up and down in the bet size. Half an hour's play at the table, waiting for favorable situations, confirmed this. When a run of favorable situations finally came, I changed from a waiting bet of $1 to the $5 to $25 range. There now was a long steady run of favorable situations before the four decks finally ran out. I won about $80. During the next two or three hours of play there were comparable runs with similar results. Altogether, I accumulated about $160. A card-expert friend, who was standing by, thought the game was so safe that he wandered away. We were soon to get an expensive education.

Shortly afterwards, a dealer against whom I had not previously played came to my table. After a few minutes the four decks became favorable. Only this time, I lost nearly every hand. Before the run ended I had lost $250. Startled and suspicious, I then watched the dealer intently.

It was conceivable that he could deal seconds out of the particular shoe being employed. But how could he identify the top card? Peeking seemed impossible; hence shiners were ruled out. What about marked cards? I watched the dealer's eyes but he never glanced at the part of the back of the card which was exposed in the oval hole.

The four decks were about average during the next ten runs so I dropped back to $1 waiting bets. However, I was losing on nearly every hand! I then began to count and found that, in 26 hands, I lost 24, tied one, and won one! The odds against losing at least 24 of 26 hands by chance alone are* about 2,000,000 to 1! I could not believe it. Could I be so tired that I could not count? To be safe, I counted the next group of wins and losses by putting chips in little piles. I also was obvious about it so that the dealer would be sure to notice. I wanted to see whether he would alter his behavior. He did not. On the next 14 hands I lost 12, tied one, and won one. The odds against losing at least 36 out of 40 hands by chance alone are about 250,000,000 to one! I was baffled—how did he do it?

And then I noticed an odd thing. The dealer, in picking up his winning pair of Tens, slipped a small card from my hand between them. An accident? I soon found that the used cards were being stacked "low-high, low-high." Then I watched them come out on the deal. Six of us picked up our hands and we all had (*10,3*), (*10,2*), (*10,6*), (*9,5*), etc. I quit playing now and watched the fellow ply his trade. He picked up the cards so smoothly that his interlacing of high and low was almost unnoticeable. He preserved the order of the cards through the shuffle (a false shuffle that looks like a real shuffle, but does not affect the cards, is standard equipment with card sharps). When he dealt, he never needed to peek or use marked cards. He knew where the cards were: just where he had stacked them.

The casino had dealt with my earlier run of "luck" rather promptly and brutally. I decided to find out whether this was casino policy. I observed that this dealer generally played at the table that was getting the most action. Further, most of the other dealers were less skilled. It seemed likely that they were not "in the know." Sure enough, when I made

* Readers who attempt to calculate this figure by assuming that the probabilities of winning and losing are each about 0.5 will get a figure of a little over 200,000 to 1. However, the probability of a tie is nearly 0.1 and should be taken into account. When this is done and we ask, what is the chance of at least 24 losses in 26 hands, with the probability of each loss about 0.45 and the probability of each nonloss (equals tie or win) about 0.55, we get the figure of 2,000,000 to 1.

$1 bets at their tables I was not cheated, and the deck-stacker busied himself elsewhere. I struck up conversations with a number of these dealers to check my speculations. I asked whether there had been any winners lately. A few dealers remembered only one such person in the last week (the others remembered none). This person was supposed to have made $500. I guessed that he must have played only a short time and bet fairly large. Sure enough, the dealers said he bet $25 and $50 ($100 on doubling down and pair splitting) and played only a short time. Thus his win corresponded to $20 betting $1 to $2: he was lucky and besides he probably quit before the big guns could reach him.

I have since found the high-low pickup is also being used at many, many other casinos. In my judgment it is the most widespread single method of dealer cheating now in use. Here is a test that will give you an idea of the power of the high-low pickup. Let Aces, *10*'s, and *9*'s be high. Let *2* through *7* be low. Let two *8*'s be high and two, be low. Stack the deck low-high, low-high. Now deal hands to an imaginary player and to yourself as dealer. Deal so that the player gets low-low and you get high-high. If the order of the deck is low-high, this is automatic. If it is high-low, you can deal seconds. You should win virtually every hand. We will not go into the many refinements and variations, both in cheating and in defense by the player (he too knows where the cards are and can occasionally revenge himself) when a stacked deck is used.

Instead, we recommend that you get out of that game immediately.

Deck Stacking: The Seven-Card Stepup

One afternoon I was playing head-on and betting from $10 to $100. After I had played three or four decks, I noticed that the dealer had started each deck with two hands, one of which was twenty-one and the other twenty. More amazing, his twenty-one was composed each time of the Ace of Spades and the same Ten-value card, the Queen of Clubs. At my elbow, *employed in a private capacity,* was Mr. Michael MacDougall, one of the world's outstanding detectors of card cheats and a special investigator for the Nevada Gaming Control Board. (The rest of this chapter is drawn from our experiences on a trip which followed by nine months the trip described in Chapter 6. We were to spend twelve hours a day for eight days playing dozens of the principal Nevada casinos.) Mr. McDougall told me that the dealer had set up a card sequence of *7,8,9,10,10,J,Q, K,A*. The sequence was preserved during the shuffle. It is a standard technique of card cheats to shuffle a deck repeatedly in such a way that some preselected clump of cards is left undisturbed. The sequence was "bridged," meaning that it was bent down the center, lengthwise so that, when placed face down on a table, the center did not touch the table.

The dealer had left the sequence near the middle of the deck when he offered it to me to cut. An unaware player will generally cut the deck so that the bridged cards become the top cards. Try it yourself and see.

Knowledge of the bridge may prove useful to you. For example, I enjoy and frequently play the *game* of bridge. Occasionally my wife and I get "stuck" for an evening with a boring pair of opponents from whom we cannot readily excuse ourselves. Here is one solution to this problem. Roll up a commanding lead (if you can). Then bridge the four Aces when your turn to shuffle arrives. Shuffle the deck thoroughly and then show your opponents how you can cut the four Aces out of the deck at your whim. You will find that the game ends, politely of course. Somehow, you never have those opponents again.

Let us return to our story. After I had cut the *7* to the top, the cards dealt were: *8* to me, *9* to the dealer, *10* to me,

10 to the dealer. He held 19, I held 18. On the next hand the cards went *J* to me, *Q* to the dealer, *K* to me, *A* to the dealer. His natural beat my twenty.

He stacked these cards as he picked them up into the same sequence. With the next deck the situation repeated itself. The reader can easily convince himself that the same card stack is effective against two or three players.

At this particular casino, when the dealers went off duty, they put the decks in their pockets. When the new dealers came on, they took decks out of their pockets. We found out that they were going off and setting the "stepup" into the deck.

The story is told that a dealer in Newport, Kentucky, was the inventor of this stepup and that he was so proud of his achievement that he considered demanding royalties from the casinos using it.

I tried various defenses against the stepup. First I insured against all dealer Aces on the first two hands of each deck. This was not satisfactory for the dealer rearranged the sequence so that his Ace was in the hole. Next I tried betting low on the first two hands. After paying my initial tax on each deck I thought I might be able to win the remaining honest hands.

However, the deck almost always remained unfavorable! After some thought, I figured out why. The ratio of others to Tens is normally 2.25. But when the particular stepup passed by, it took five Tens and only four others with it. The ratio was then 32/11 or 2.9. This is so far from favorable that only rarely do chance fluctuations change it to favorable. Thus, the stepup not only steals the first two hands outright from the player, it robs the deck of good cards and the player loses the majority of succeeding hands played from this gutted residue.

I also tried cutting the deck in unusual ways, which I varied randomly. I succeeded in burying the stepup in random areas of the deck. However, this hurt, rather than helped me. Notice that if the stepup is buried in the deck, sometimes some one of the first four cards may end up being the top card of the remainder of the deck from which the next hand will be dealt. If it is the *7* or *8,* I lose two successive hands. If it is the *9,* I lose one unit and win one and one-half units (unless the dealer second-deals the Ace to himself!). If it is the first Ten, we "push," or tie; this is a total loss of one and one-half units in the four possibilities. Thus, on the average I shall lose 3/8 unit when the stepup goes by.

This may seem much cheaper than losing the first two hands outright. But it was not. I was playing the Tens strategy and, before the stepup occurred, the deck tended to seem abnormally Ten-rich (because the stepup is). Thus I had very large bets down when the stepup came through. They were large enough so that 3/8 of one of them greatly exceeded two of the small initial bets.

Much the same objection holds to the next defense I attempted: spotting the stepup and cutting it in half.

There are many other sequences which have the same effect as the stepup I have just described.

A closely related and much more innocent-appearing stacking idea, which does not seem to be currently fashionable, is to let the deck begin each time with a sequence of Tens. Then, everyone holds 20 and ties the dealer on the first round. However, succeeding rounds are played from a Ten-poor deck. The effect is the same as though several Tens were removed from the deck before play.

The shuffling technique used to preserve the stepup can be used to convince an onlooker that the deck is not being false-shuffled. The dealer can even square it up after each shuffle. However, a high-low sequence of considerable length can be preserved this way.

One greedy, blond dealer against whom I played briefly

was preserving a high-low clump *twenty* cards long. When I called her attention to the clump, she refused to shuffle to destroy it.

Often, one sees a blackjack table standing empty, attended by a dealer and awaiting customers. It is common practice at such tables to leave the deck spread out face up. Presumably this is so the player will see that all the cards are there. If the deck is newly opened and the cards are in their original order, it is possible to easily tell whether or not any cards are missing. It is not easy to tell this when the cards have been mixed up. And as soon as you sit down the deck is scooped up, shuffled, and brought into play; therefore you have no time to check the deck. Mr. Michael MacDougall, who was protecting me at the time that we discovered the stepup being used, observed that if we stood back from such an empty table and examined the deck we could find the stepups all laid out and waiting. He took me to a suspect casino. At the first table we approached we saw the stepup. We bet $1 and the dealer offered us the deck to cut, without even bothering to shuffle. As expected, we cut the stepup to the top and the dealer received 20, followed by 21. We commented on how we had been cheated by a stepup and the dealer laughed happily, proud of his handiwork and that someone finally appreciated it.

Anchor Men

One large hotel on the Las Vegas strip seemed to be completely free from cheating. After I had won a couple of hundred dollars in half an hour, playing $5 to $50, one of the pit bosses jokingly asked how the system was working. The card expert who was protecting me told him "up and down, like an elevator." Since the pit boss was friendly enough and we were running out of places in which to play, we adopted the following policy with this hotel. Bet $5 to $50 and stop playing after we had won $200 or played forty-five minutes, whichever was sooner. Forty-five minutes was short enough so that I could fully recover in a few minutes from the strains of counting, refreshed and relaxed. If we stopped at $200, our win was small enough, compared to ordinary chance fluctuations, to seem to be just a little luck.

(The reader may be puzzled at the contrast between this timid low-scale betting and the earlier test reported in Chapter 6. Conditions in Nevada seemed to have changed drastically between these two times. On this trip we learned that if we won more than $250 to $500 or placed a single bet above $50 to $100, we did so at our peril.)

This casino welcomed us back the next few times we came. We proceeded to beat them eight times in a row. We were busily at work on a ninth win when the pit boss called over our dealer and told him something. My friend Mr. MacDougall overheard the dealer say "All right, I'll give it to him." When the dealer returned we asked him what he was going to give me. He only smiled. Our eyes locked onto the dealer's hands and eyes. He did not do anything suspicious. Puzzled, we watched and played. In a few minutes an individual, who would have otherwise seemed inconspicuous, came steaming down the aisle behind our row of blackjack tables. He was passing our table at high speed when the pit boss whistled. He made a sharp turn on his heel and plunked down in the seat to my right. I cut my bets and awaited developments.

We immediately noticed that the dealer now might be peeking, but he did not deal any seconds. The new player watched the dealer's eyes before he decided whether to draw or stand. I tried to see his cards when the bets were being settled in order that I could see if he were following a consistent strategy. But he either threw his cards in face down or the dealer picked them up so that I saw only their backs. Finally, I got two glances at this fellow's cards.

He stood on hard 8 once and drew on hard 19 the second time! Further scrutiny on successive hands confirmed the fact that the dealer was peeking and that if he wanted me to get the top card, he signalled the new player to stand. If he wanted to keep the top card from me (for example, suppose I doubled down and he saw it was a Nine or Ten), he signalled the new player, termed an anchor man, to draw. Thus an anchor man makes the dealing of seconds unnecessary. With marked cards even the peek would become unnecessary.

The dealer could easily infer from my behavior, formed through long habit, whether I was going to double down, draw, stand, or split a pair. It is thus a useful art in casino blackjack to be able to play with a poker face. An easier way to combat an anchor man is to wait until your turn to even look at your cards. In this way, you cannot possibly help the dealer who uses an anchor man.

We moved to another table, the one farthest from where we were. I sat so that a player already at that table was on my right, occupying the anchor man's future seat. The word was passed to the dealer and the anchor man waited patiently. In a few minutes the player on my right left and the anchor man plopped down. We left. The fun was over in that casino.

Alternatively, the anchor man may be seated on the dealer's right. He then stands or draws according to signals from the dealer. This enables the dealer, whose turn is next, to draw for himself more desirable cards. The entire table loses to the dealer's superior cards, in contrast to the first version of the anchor man in which only one player seems singled out for hard luck.

We had several additional incidents with anchor men in other casinos. They suggest to me that Nevada, a state without sea coast, has the biggest "navy" of any state in the union.

The Gratuitous Peek

When the dealer has a Ten up, he immediately checks his hole card to see whether he has a natural. When he has an Ace up, he first asks the players if they want insurance (assuming the insurance rule is being used) and only after this is decided does he check his hole card. When he has any other card up, there is no reason for him to check his hole card before his turn to play. I have on a number of occasions seen dealers check their hole card when an Ace was up before they offered the players insurance. They then tried by their actions and manner to influence the player. If they had a natural they either would not offer insurance or they would rush the player. If they had no natural, they gave the player plenty of time and even hinted with their facial expressions that insurance was wise. Once in a while I have seen dealers look at their hole card immediately when they had neither a Ten nor an Ace up. They then continue to peek until they find a card they need, which they hold for themselves by dealing seconds.

Mechanics on Call

A (card) mechanic is a skilled cheat who accomplishes his ends by sleight of hand. Some larger casinos have their own mechanics working as dealers on the regular shifts. Since mechanics are paid much better than ordinary dealers, a casino which cheats will, for reasons of economy, hire only as many as pay for themselves by the extra revenue. Often there is only one mechanic per shift. One morning I was betting $10 to $100 and winning. After a while, the dealer went off duty and his relief came on. Suddenly the pit boss rushed over, scolded the relief, sent him to another table, and made our dealer stay on. A few minutes later another dealer the pit boss had summoned relieved our dealer. The new dealer was, according to the expert who was protecting me, obviously a mechanic. We could not see any definite cheating, only suspicious moves. But, good mechanics can often conceal their move from the most skilled eyes, leaving only a few suspicious side effects. We immediately lost nearly every bet. At the $10 level we lost a couple of hundred dollars of our winnings in a few minutes.

We walked across the street to a smaller casino, one presumably too poor to have a mechanic on duty. Betting $5 to $50, we were well ahead after twenty minutes. The pit boss was grimly hostile. Then he made a phone call. More time passed and then we noticed from our watches that it was time for our dealer to go off shift, yet he was not. In "a city without clocks," always carry a watch in order to see that your dealers are being changed at after what you observe to be the regular length of time for a shift, and at no other time. A break in the pattern indicates trouble.

Our dealer had been on duty thirty-seven minutes (thirty was normal in this casino) when a man dressed in a white shirt and black pants like the other dealers, but without the apron of that casino, hastened through the front door and up to our table. He immediately began to deal. We spotted him as a mechanic. With a smile he purred "Would you gentlemen like a drink?" The pit boss became relaxed and in good spirits. A wave of friendliness seemed to pervade the grim, barren, midmorning desolation of the place. We left.

Miscellaneous Methods

We have previously discussed both the turnover and the removal or addition of cards to the deck. Another method, like these fairly rarely used, might be termed "arbitrary house shuffling." The dealer may play half way through the deck and, seeing that the cards favoring the house are mostly gone, shuffle and bring them back into play. When the deck runs out at the end of a deal, I have seen dealers refuse to pay off, immediately, the winning hands involving good cards, for example, (*A,10*), (*10,10*), (*10,9*), but instead pay off the others, rake these cards in, and shuffle. After the shuffle, the good hands would be paid and placed on the bottom of the deck. The next few hands would therefore be dealt from a deck that is relatively poor in Aces, Tens, and Nines.

There are so many ways for the dealer to cheat that we can only give a brief introduction to the subject here. The interested reader can study it in much greater detail in the many references that are available [13, 17, 22, 31, 38]. Many interesting facts were also uncovered during a Senate investigation of gambling in the fall of 1961 [21, 26].

Those readers who are shocked at the level of development of card cheating reported here might be interested in knowing that cheating at cards was already a fairly well developed skill in the sixteenth century. To quote Cardano*:

"As for those who use marked cards, some mark them at the bottom, some at the top, and some at the sides. The first kind are marked quite close to the bottom and may be either rough or smooth or hard; the second are marked with color and with slight imprints with a knife; while on the edges cards can be marked with a figure, a rough spot, with interwoven knots or humps, or with grooves hollowed out with a file. Some players examine the appearance of a card by means of mirrors placed in their rings. . . .

. . . There are also some who smear the cards with soap so that they may slide easily and slip past one another. . . ."

Despite all our warnings and the frequency with which dealers cheat, there are a number of casinos that are scrupu-

* This quotation appears through the courtesy of the Princeton University Press and is reprinted from Cardano, The Gambling Scholar, by Øystein Ore, pages 210, 211.

lously honest. Our purpose in this chapter is to make the reader acutely aware of the dangers of cheating and to give him enough knowledge so that, in most cases, he will be able to spot it and change casinos before suffering a serious loss. It should now be evident that it is suicide to play in a place that cheats; you have virtually no hope whatsoever of winning.

You have completed your basic education in how to win at blackjack. You have one or two winning strategies, you have vicariously seen one of them in action, and you have some knowledge about how to protect yourself against the main danger, cheating. You are ready for casino play.

Recommendations for Cleaning Up the Game of Blackjack

Cheating by the dealer at blackjack is *easier* than in most casino gambling games. The game is fast, the dealer continually has his hands on the cards, and the players are kept busy making decisions. Cheating by the dealer at blackjack is *safer* than in most other casino gambling games. Courts of law usually need concrete, material evidence of cheating, such as loaded dice, electromagnetic roulette wheels, or marked cards. However, in blackjack the variety of alternate ways in which the dealer can cheat the player makes marked cards passé. It is difficult for a regulatory agency such as the Nevada Gaming Control Board to get a court conviction of a casino for cheating simply on the testimony of innumerable casino customers, some of whose reports are clouded by inconsistencies, errors, prejudices, and suspicions, and few of whom are established card experts. My experiences lead me to believe dealer cheating at casino blackjack is perhaps more *widespread* than in most of the other games.

The recommendations which I give here will, if they are enacted into a set of enforceable regulations, make every dealer cheating method described in this book virtually impossible.

1. A clear plastic bin should be attached to the top of the blackjack table on the dealer's right. As cards are used, they should be placed face down in this bin. That this prevents the turnover was originally pointed out to me by Mr. Michael MacDougall, special investigator for the Nevada Gaming Control Board. Several Nevada casinos have already taken this step.

2. Plastic cards with borders should be required by law. Plastic cards are more troublesome to crimp and they "scrape" more loudly when a second is dealt. They are unpopular with mechanics. Cards with borders make second dealing more difficult. A few casinos now use plastic cards with borders.

3. If the dealer does not want to deal all the way through the deck, that is, if he wants to shuffle up, or if a player calls for a shuffle, the unused cards should be spread face up for a long enough time before the new shuffle so that they can be counted by anyone interested in verifying the deck. Both players and inspectors for the Gaming Control Board should be interested in doing this. Being able to count the cards to make sure none have been removed is even more important in two-deck and four-deck games for in these games cards can also be *added* safely.

Otherwise the dealer could remove some of the cards from the deck and he could conceal this fact simply by shuffling each time before the end of the deck. If any player noticed that certain cards never appeared, he would be forced to assume that, by chance, they always happened to fall in the unused and unseen part of the deck. To make this more convenient, after the deck is cut the joker should be placed face up on the bottom of the deck so that the former bottom card is concealed. A card should not be burned. This also prevents another method of cheating which works as follows. The dealer bridges (a special case of what is known as crimping, the general term for bending or warping cards) one or more Tens or Aces. Then when the deck is cut one of these cards is almost always on top, and is burned. This robbing of the deck costs the player an average of about 0.6 per cent of his bet per hand played.

At this time, some casinos do use the joker in this way as the bottom card.

4. A smooth, hard rectangle should be attached to the table in front of the dealer. After he cuts the deck and shuffles the two halves together, he should be required to square the deck sharply and completely against this hard surface. This prevents the false shuffle, in which the dealer pushes the two halves of the deck approximately together and then pulls them back apart again.

5. The dealer's shuffling in such a way that a clump of cards of length five or more is never broken up should be considered by the courts as prima facie evidence of cheating. A minimum should be set to the number of shuffles that is large enough so that the persistence of clumps could not reasonably be expected to occur by accident.

6. The gratuitous peek by the dealer should also be considered by the courts as prima facie evidence of cheating.

7. The plastic cards with borders should be dealt from a clear plastic dealing box or shoe. The clear plastic will make gaffing (that is, rigging the box so it is crooked) more difficult. Dealing boxes are generally thought to protect the player against seconds. However, dealing boxes which are specifically designed to assist in the dealing of a second are well known. The shoe should be such that the cards lie face down, rather than on edge. Since the top of the top card has borders and is visible through the clear plastic of the shoe, a second will be readily visible in any case. Further, the slit through which the top card is drawn should be at the extreme

top of the shoe and should be only slightly wider than one card in thickness but thinner than two. Thereupon, a potential second would be held below the lower lip of the slit by the thickness of the top card and could not be drawn out. The shoe should be spring-loaded and the cards should fit the inside dimensions of the shoe snugly. The shoe also makes peeking impossible. The adoption of the particular shoe we have described, not just "any" shoe, is the most important single countermeasure against dealer cheating in blackjack.

8. The format by which the used cards are picked up by the dealer should be specifically detailed in order that no variation is possible. The intent is to exclude various forms of stacking, particularly the high-low pickup.

For example, hands that bust could be picked up at once and placed in the bin, and before any cards are played to the next hand. When the dealer plays his hand out, if he busts, his hand is also put in the bin at once. Then the player hands are paid and picked up, one at a time, from left to right. If the dealer does not bust, payment of the player hands is settled, and they are picked up, *one at a time,* again from left to right. Lastly, the dealer picks up his hand.

Not only must the order in which hands are picked up be prescribed, there must be no rearrangement of the naturally occurring order of individual cards in a given hand, as it lies on the table. If the individual cards are not touching, they should be picked up one at a time, from left to right, that is, in such a manner that the left-most card is face up on top of the hand after it is picked up, the next left-most is next, etc.

The regulatory agency could publicize this new art and carry out brief one-hour instruction classes in it for all dealers.

9. I have often been the near-victim of faulty pay-offs by the dealer. In each of the twenty-five or so instances that

I have experienced, dealers have always erred in favor of the house. Thus one can hardly ascribe all these errors to "chance." I have seen many other players cheated in this manner. Its occurrence is most prevalent on a weekend night when the tables are packed and a very fast dealer is on, picking up and paying off so fast that one often scarcely has time to compare his total with that of the dealer. This too should be prima facie evidence of guilt in the courts.

10. The local regulatory agency should be empowered to carry out surprise inspections and temporary confiscations of the gambling equipment in the casino. The fact that this is done should be widely publicized in such a way that the general public will welcome these inspections in their presence, as an additional assurance that they are being constantly protected, rather than as an indication of any foul play by the casino.

11. All of these regulations should be printed and distributed as required reading for all casino personnel. It should also be required by law that these regulations be posted conspicuously in the casino for the benefit of the customer. Instructions on how the customer should proceed to report violations to the local regulatory agency should also be included.

12. As new cheating methods to circumvent these regulations are devised and uncovered, the regulations should be extended to eliminate them.

Some people may argue that new cheating methods will always be invented and that, therefore, attempts to prevent cheating by regulations are bound to fail. Instead they say we must depend simply on the integrity of the management. If we apply this argument to our society as a whole, we would have to conclude that all laws should be abandoned since someone will always succeed in breaking them. The argument is thus fallacious.

In the case of blackjack the regulations will greatly increase the difficulty of cheating. Greater skill will be required and fewer people will be capable of it. As time passes and more loopholes are plugged, cheating, though still possible, will be reduced to a negligible level.

We have remarked that some casinos have adopted some of our proposed measures. This helps but it prevents only some types of cheating.

We recommend to regulatory agencies, such as the Nevada Gaming Control Board, that they see that these measures are promptly and completely adopted.

8

Rules Variations

Up until now, we have always considered blackjack as being played according to the typical set of rules outlined in Chapter 2. Now each of the rules given there is commonly used in many, and generally in most, casinos. Although each rule has numerous variations and although a given casino may use most of the rules in the typical set, it seldom uses every single one of them. The rules variations discussed in this chapter are a summary of the information which was obtained by the author as follows. Detailed written questionnaires on rules were filled out by thirteen casinos. The author personally visited and questioned a hundred other casinos. Friends and acquaintances who have played in various parts of the world contributed information from their knowledge and experiences.

It is the purpose of this chapter to teach the reader to judge the effect on his advantage, of the variations selected by any casino. Thus the player can evaluate how much better or worse than the typical rules, are the rules of the casino at which he plays. The person who plays a lot of blackjack will often be able to save himself considerable sums of money simply by walking across the street.

As time passes, this chapter should increase steadily in importance. As more and more system players beat the (honest) casinos, they will be forced to introduce variations in their rules which are harmful to the player.

We shall discuss in turn those variations not considered in detail elsewhere, using subheadings similar to those in Chapter 2. Then the results will be summarized in a table. It must be kept in mind that the figures stipulated throughout are only approximate. This is necessary for the following reason. In general, the effect of a single rules variation, for example the restriction of doubling down to a total of (hard) eleven, is influenced by the presence or absence of other rules variations. The effect also varies with the composition of the deck. For playing purposes, it is generally sufficient to use the approximate effect, when the basic strategy is being used, as an over-all estimate in any situation.

The Pack

Two packs shuffled together reduce the player's advantage by 0.21 per cent. Four packs shuffled together hurt the player somewhat more (about 0.35 per cent).

The mathematical reason for this is that dealing cards from the deck to construct hands is sampling without replacement [9]. Thus, even though the original proportions of the ten types of cards are the same regardless of the number of decks that are shuffled together, the effect of withdrawing cards has a smaller effect on the proportions of the remaining cards when the number of decks is increased. According to probability theory, the chance of being dealt a natural in the case of one complete, well-shuffled deck is $(16 \times 4 \times 2)/(52 \times 51)$ or 4.83 per cent. In the case of two decks it drops to $(32 \times 8 \times 2)/(104 \times 103)$ or 4.78 per cent. With four decks it is $(64 \times 16 \times 2)/(208 \times 207)$ or 4.76 per cent.

The best strategy was completely recalculated under the supposition that two decks were being used. The best strategy for two decks involves only a few small changes from the basic strategy of Chapter 3. We list these changes in the interests of completeness even though the effect on the advantage of the player who ignores them is negligible.

When the dealer shows an Ace, do not double down on hard 11 and, change your soft standing number to 19. When the dealer shows a 7, do not split 6's. When the dealer shows a 6, split 4's. When the dealer shows a 4, do not double down on soft 14. When the dealer shows a 2, do not double down on hard 9 unless it consists of (7,2).

The Draw

Some casinos have altered the dealer's rules for standing:

1. *Soft-seventeen rule.* The dealer's soft standing number is 18, rather than 17. This hurts the player by 0.19 per cent.

2. *Ace-only soft-seventeen rule.* When the dealer's up card is an Ace, his soft standing number is 18. Otherwise, it is 17. It actually hurts the dealer slightly to draw on soft 17 when he has *2* through *6* up (as is later shown in Table 8.1), so this is a better variation for the house. It hurts the player by 0.22 per cent.

3. *Optional soft-seventeen rule.* The dealer can stand or draw, as he wishes, to soft 17. This is at least as good for the house as variation 2. The dealer can use it to play this variation until he sees an obvious situation where he should draw (if he has *2* through *6* up) or should not draw (if he has *A* up) and thus make further gains. Since the dealers

using this will vary in cleverness, we can only describe the casino gain as 0.22 per cent +.

We completely recalculated the best strategy in the case that the dealer's soft standing number is 18 rather than 17. As might be expected, there are some changes in the player's best strategy that result from the changes in the dealer's strategy. The interesting fact is that these changes in the basic strategy are few, and furthermore, they may be neglected without appreciable loss to the player. The changes are: *When the dealer shows an Ace, change your soft standing number to 19. When the dealer shows a 6, split 4's and also, double down on soft 19.*

These considerations suggest a rather subtle question. The soft-seventeen rules variations favor the house when it faces a player using best play. Do these rules variations also favor the house against players using other strategies? By how much? The answer to this question is involved, as a little discussion will suggest. The answer, however, is perhaps surprising.

Note first that if the player has a total of less than 17, the dealer can only lose by drawing on soft 17 because, if he stood, he would certainly win. However, if he draws, he may get a hard total below seventeen and, on drawing to reach 17, he might bust. The situation is reversed if the player has a total above 17. The dealer is sure to lose if he does not draw but may be able to win by a fortunate draw. Thus, in this instance the dealer can only gain by drawing. If the player has precisely 17, the dealer starts with a tie. He gains by drawing if, and only if, his chance to improve his total exceeds the chance that he will bust.

Now consider the variation where the house draws on soft 17 only when the dealer has an Ace up. Table 8.1 shows that this variation gains for the house when the player uses the basic strategy, namely, a hard standing number of 17 and a soft standing number of 18. By the preceding discussion, the house gains still more by this rule when facing a player who has both hard and soft standing numbers of 18.

At the other extreme is the player who always stands on 12. For such a player, the soft-seventeen rules probably† are advantageous (especially the one requiring the dealer to hit all soft 17's) because this player generally has such low totals that the dealer's gain in achieving a still higher total than 17, which will probably win, is more than offset by his increased chance of busting. Even in the less extreme case of a player using the basic strategy, when the dealer shows a *6*, the player stands on hard 12 and soft 18, and the dealer drawing on soft 17 loses for the house (see Table 8.1).

We see, therefore, that even though a variation may favor the house against some strategies, it may hurt the house against others. Thus a rules variation can, from the viewpoint of the casino, be either favorable or unfavorable, depending on the strategies currently favored by the players betting the bulk of the money.

Table 8.1 lists the player's advantage against various up cards of the dealer when the dealer stands on soft 17 and also when he stands on soft 18.

TABLE 8.1.

Player's advantage* when dealer stands on	Dealer shows					
	2	**3**	**4**	**5**	**6**	**A**
soft **17**	0.0944	0.1297	0.1759	0.2294	0.2365	−0.3640
soft **18**	0.0946	0.1299	0.1768	0.2296	0.2391	−0.3929

* The advantage is listed assuming the player uses the best possible strategy and that the dealer has not yet checked for a natural. Since the rules are equivalent when the dealer shows *7* through *10* (soft 17 is impossible), these up cards are omitted from the table.

† We have not carried through the detailed calculation required to give a precise figure. The calculation is lengthy but not difficult. It involves the construction of a table of player's probabilities for these player's standing numbers.

Splitting Pairs

1. *Further splitting* of all pairs.* The player gains 0.04 per cent.

2. *Further splitting of all pairs except Aces.* The player gains 0.03 per cent.

3. *Further splitting of all pairs except Aces and Tens of different rank.* Some casinos distinguish between, for example, (*J,J*) and (*J,Q*). For purposes of splitting, they consider the former to be a pair and the latter not to be. Unwittingly, they do the average player a favor with this little "technicality," for splitting Tens is rarely advisable, yet it is an error frequently made by players. The player still gains 0.03 per cent.

4. *Further splitting of all pairs except Aces and Tens.* The player gains 0.03 per cent.

In a game in which two or more decks are used, some casinos limit to four the number of hands that can be obtained by resplitting.

5. *Drawing any number of cards to split Aces.* This rule is 0.22 per cent in favor of the player.

6. *Aces may not be split.* This hurts the player by 0.15 per cent.

Restrictions on Doubling Down

1. *No doubling down on soft totals.* The house gains 0.09 per cent.

2. *No doubling down after pairs are split.* The house gains 0.11 per cent.

3. *No doubling down on hard Nine.* The house gains

* Suppose a player splits, say, a pair of *8*'s, and that on one of the split *8*'s he is dealt as his second card another *8*. Further splitting refers to the possibility of splitting this new pair of *8*'s to form a third hand and to continue the process, if desired, if further *8*'s are dealt as the second hole card.

0.11 per cent, and considerably more in a Ten-rich situation.

4. *No doubling down on hard Ten.* The house gains 0.52 per cent and considerably more in a Ten-rich situation.

5. *No doubling down on hard eleven.* The house gains 0.77 per cent on the average but the gain is considerably more in a Ten-rich situation.

Redoubling

Some of the casinos in Cuba (not now in existence) and a large casino in Canada (which is operating illegally but under the protection of local authorities) had an interesting variation on doubling down. After the player doubled down and drew a third card, he could, if desired, double down again; that is, he could redouble, drawing a fourth card.

The best basic strategy, when the redoubling rule is in effect, is quite interesting and easily determined by the same methods used to find the basic strategy of Chapter 3. Since the redoubling rule is rarely found at the present time, we have not calculated the precise gain which it gives to the player. However, this gain is considerable, as the following discussion indicates.

The weakness of ordinary doubling down is that the player can draw only one more card. This restriction is largely relaxed by the redoubling rule. For example, suppose the player doubles down on hard *9* when the dealer shows a *5*. If he draws a *2*, for a total of 11, he can now redouble. The average gain in this situation resulting from redoubling turns out to be approximately 103 per cent of the player's original bet! It varies slightly depending on whether his original hard 9 was made up of (*7,2*), (*6,3*), or (*5,4*).

The increased value of the doubling down rule also leads to more frequent doubling down. Taking the basic strategy as an illustration, suppose the player has hard 8 and the dealer shows a *6*. The player's advantage, if he doubles down, happens to be 10.4 per cent. If he draws correctly, it is 12.8 per cent. If he has a pair of Fours and splits them, his advantage with best play is 12.6 per cent. Thus the basic strategy recommends that he draw. However, if redoubling is permitted, the advantage from doubling down jumps to approximately 29 per cent and doubling down becomes the recommended strategy. Calculation shows that doubling down is even preferable now on a total of hard 7!

Thus redoubling increases considerably the number of doubling down situations. Further, when these situations arise, the gains are often so phenomenal that the effect on the player's advantage is considerable even after averaging over all hands played. He probably has an over-all edge over the casino of the order of magnitude of between one and three per cent.

There is a famous story connected with redoubling. Two gamblers* from the United States visited the Cuban casinos in 1958. They were allowed to bet to a very high limit, to redouble, and also, after a pair split, to double the bet on each hand. Even though the casinos shuffled well before the end of the deck(s), with their edge, these players were able to accumulate $224,000 in a few days. Immediately after this great win they were not permitted to leave the country but were held several days before they were released.

Insurance

1. *No insurance*. The effect on the player's advantage is rather different from the usual effect of the other rules. The presence or absence of insurance does not matter for players using the basic strategy. With the Five-count strategy one should insure when the *5*'s are gone and neither hole

* One of them is a friend and personally conveyed details of the story to me.

card is a *10* and otherwise not insure. Using the Ten-count strategy, the player should insure when the ratio of others to Tens is less than 2.0 and not otherwise. In this circumstance, the effect of forbidding insurance gradually increases as the ratio drops until, with a ratio of 1.00 it cuts 1.6 per cent from the 9.2 per cent advantage of the Ten-count player. For details see Figure 5.1. With the usual betting schemes, the average over all loss for the Ten-count player is of the order of 1 per cent.

2. *Insurance when the dealer shows a Ten.* This is a rare rule: some casinos reportedly allow the player to insure against a natural when the dealer shows a Ten. If the dealer has an Ace underneath, the insurance bet pays 10 to 1. If he does not have an Ace in the hole, the player's side bet is lost. With a full deck, this bet wins 4 times in 51, for a gain of 40 units, and loses 47 times in 51 for a loss of 47 units. The average rate of loss is 7/51 or 13.7 per cent. If the player counts Tens, this bet is favorable only in certain Ten-poor situations, namely when twice the number of non-Tens exceeds nine times the number of Tens. Therefore it is of little interest to a Ten-count player. If the player counts Aces also, though, then this bet is favorable whenever ten times the number of unplayed Aces exceeds the number of nonAces. This is possible in Ten-rich situations, when a big bet has been placed by the Ten-count player, and in these cases may be quite valuable.

Bonuses

Some casinos pay lump sums ("bonuses") for special holdings. These sums are generally quite small and, since the special holdings are quite rare, the net effect, though favorable to the player, is minuscule. Here are some specimens we have found.

1. *Seven or more cards totalling exactly 21:* $25.00.
2. *Seven cards totalling less than 21:* $2.50.

3. *Eight cards totalling less than 21:* $5.00.

4. *Ace and Jack of spades as hole cards:* $5.00. This happens on an average of one hand in 1,326, when one deck is used. With two decks it happens on an average of one hand in 1,339. Here is another example of a difference between one deck and two decks.

5. *Six, Seven, and Eight of the same suit:* $5.00. This occurs less than once every 5,000 hands.

6. *Three Sevens:* $5.00. This also happens less than once every 5,000 hands.

Comparison of Casino Rules

Let us now summarize the effects of the rules variations as shown in Table 8.2.

I have frequently seen casinos which allowed both the resplitting of all pairs and doubling down on any number of cards. In these casinos the player gains (0.04 + 0.20) or 0.24 per cent; this amounts to about $1 profit for each $400 worth of action.

There are also a number of casinos at the other extreme which forbid doubling down on totals other than hard ten and eleven, forbid doubling down after pair splitting, have the soft-seventeen rule and have no insurance; this hurts the player using the basic strategy by (0.11 + 0.09) + (0.11 + 0.19 +0.0) or 0.50 per cent. Since the basic strategy player never insures, forbidding insurance has no effect on his advantage. By contrast the Ten-count player often insures. If we estimate the average loss when insurance is forbidden at 1 per cent, he loses about (1.00 + 0.50) or 1.5 per cent, of his "action" at such casinos. His rate of profit drops to about two thirds of its former amount.

TABLE 8.2. *Approximate Effect of Common Rules Variations on Player's Advantage.*

Rules variations	Player's loss or gain (in per cent)
forbid doubling down on	
hard eleven	– 0.77 *
hard ten	– 0.52 *
hard nine	– 0.11 *
all soft totals	– 0.09 *
all totals after pair splitting	– 0.11 *
allow doubling down on any three cards	+ 0.19 *
allow doubling down on any number of cards	+ 0.20 *
allow redoubling	1 to 3 †
four decks	– 0.35
two decks	– 0.21
soft-seventeen rule	– 0.19
Ace only soft-seventeen rule	– 0.22
optional soft-seventeen rule	– (0.22 +)
pair splitting	
further splitting of all pairs	0.04
further splitting of all pairs except Aces	0.03 †
drawing any number of cards to split Aces	0.22 *
no splitting of Aces	– 0.15 *
forbid insurance	0 to 1.6 †
allow insurance when dealer shows a Ten	small gains †
allow bonuses	small gains †

* These figures are the result of [2].
† See text.

9

Fine Points of Play

We discuss here a number of special points of play that have proved useful and have not been covered elsewhere. How to gain an advantage from seeing the burned card or the bottom card, is even valuable to players who have not gone beyond Chapter 3 and the basic strategy. The concept of teaming up with other system players is of interest to anyone who has read as far as Chapter 4. The "ultimate" strategy, the most powerful of the strategies presented in this book, is best studied after the Ten-count strategy has been learned.

The Burned Card and the Bottom Card

It frequently happens that the player glimpses either the burned card or the bottom card of the fresh deck or both. When he knows what these cards are he can change the —0.21 per cent estimate of his advantage by adding the corrections given in the "change of expectation" column of

Table 9.1. Add one such correction for each card that is seen. For example, if your expectation against the complete deck is −0.21 per cent and you see a Five burned and know that a Four is on the bottom, your expectation changes to (−0.21 + 0.82 + 0.59) or 1.2 per cent. Double your bet.

TABLE 9.1. *The Effect on the Expectation of Burning a Card.*

Card burned	Approximate change in expectation (in per cent)	Approximate expectation with typical rules and basic strategy (in per cent)
2	0.36	0.15
3	0.48	0.27
4	0.59	0.38
5	0.82	0.61
6	0.47	0.26
7	0.34	0.13
8	0.03	−0.18
9	−0.23	−0.44
10	−0.54	−0.75
A	−0.68	−0.89

Observe that 24 of the 52 cards cause enough of a change in the expectation, when burned, to give the player an appreciable advantage. If the player makes large bets in these circumstances and small bets otherwise, he will have the advantage over the casino even when he neglects card counting and uses only the basic strategy.

The Enormous Advantage of Teaming Up with Other Players

Suppose five players, each with $100, are playing at five separate tables in the same casino. The way in which play takes place at one table, presumably, in no way affects the way in which it takes place at the other tables. If the five players play for one hour each, the situation is mathematically the same as one player playing for one hour at each of the five tables. It is also the same as one player playing five times as fast.

Suppose now that the players pool their resources in the following manner. Whenever one of them is losing he borrows funds from whoever is winning. (A sixth person will often be needed to transport money from table to table.) Then the effect is as though each of the five players were backed by the entire $500. Each of the five players can bet five times as much as he could alone with only his own $100, with no increase in the risk of ruin. Each player therefore wins five times as much as he would have alone. Thus the group of five players, each contributing the same amount, is twenty-five times as strong as one player.

There is a trace of optimism to this estimate. It could happen that the capital of the team is at a low ebb and that when a player sees a favorable situation the capital to exploit it will be unavailable, being at that moment tied up by the other players. When this sort of thing occurs the net effect is that one or more of the players may have to pass up a favorable situation. This circumstance is not likely, in general, so our figure of twenty-five need only be corrected downward slightly.

If some of the players occupy the same table, the risk is greater than if they sit at different tables. The reason is that the winning or losing of players at the same table is "linked"; for example, when one player is losing the dealer tends to hold better than average hands. This means that other players at the same table are at these times on the average also losing. A similar effect occurs when one of the players is winning. The effect on the group of players is that the fluctuations in their capital are greater with consequent increase in the chances of ruin.

My experiences have convinced me that if two or more players cooperate at the same table there are considerable advantages. For example, they can guarantee that each sees the other's cards. Also, if the table is not full, they can vary the number of hands they take in a way which makes it more difficult for the dealer to avoid being end-played. I have not been able to measure these advantages but it appears possible that they are adequate compensation for the effects due to linkage.

The general rule here is that the strength of a group of players at separate tables with pooled resources is proportional to the product of the number of players and the sum of their resources. For example, suppose a group of twenty players, each putting up $500, were to descend on a single large Nevada casino, accompanied, perhaps by members of the Gaming Control Board, and certainly, by a couple of experts on cheating. The card experts could serve the additional function of transferring money where needed. The pool of twenty players would be like twenty separate players each backed by $10,000. Under average conditions they would win more than $500 each per hour. Unless stopped, the group could drain off $250,000 per 24 hours of playing time!

The "Ultimate" Strategy: A Point-Count Method of Keeping Track of All the Cards

The corrections for the burned and bottom cards probably suggested to some readers that a strategy superior to the Ten-count strategy could be devised by introducing corrections for all the cards. These separate corrections form the basis of the strategy that we shall now discuss.

First, we assign to each card a point value proportional to the effect it has when it is removed from the deck. See Table 9.2. For ease in mental calculating, these point values were chosen as whole numbers, and therefore they are only approximate.

To keep a count, the player proceeds much as in the

TABLE 9.2. *Point Values Assigned to Cards as They Are Seen.*

Card	A	2	3	4	5	6	7	8	9	10
Value	−9	5	6	8	11	6	4	0	−3	−7

Ten-count method except that he now keeps track of three numbers, (others, Tens, points), where "points" refers to the sum of the points of the cards seen so far. For example suppose the first few cards counted are, in order, *A,10,3, 5,7,4,4*. Then the count proceeds: *A*,(35,16,—9); *10*, (35,15,—16); *3*,(34,15,—10); *5*,(33,15,1); *7*,(32,15,5); *4*,(31,15,13); *4*,(30,15,21). To decide whether to insure, the player checks others/Tens as before. To make a strategy decision, the player uses Table 5.4 as before. The new feature is this: the player's advantage A is computed from the formula A = —0.21 per cent + (3.5 per cent) × (points)/(Tens + others). The figure —0.21 per cent represents the player's advantage with the basic strategy and typical rules. In the event of rules variations it is to be changed in accordance with Chapter 8.

Suppose, for example, that a Five is burned. Then A = —0.21 per cent + (3.5 per cent) × (11)/51 = —0.21 per cent + 0.75 per cent = 0.54 per cent, in rough agreement with the figure of 0.56 per cent in Table 9.1. The figures for the player's advantage given by this formula tend to be on the conservative side. They are, however, quite good in the early and middle parts of the deck but break down in the neighborhood of five or ten cards from the end. At this point the player should go back to computing his advantage from the others/Tens ratio. At this stage the points figure can be discarded if desired.

However, if you do count points all the way to the end of the deck, many interesting things can be done. First, notice that the points have been (purposely) assigned so that the total number of points in the deck is zero. Now suppose that the count is (1,1,16). This means 16 *negative* points, and two cards, remain in the deck. You can easily convince yourself that the only way this can happen is if the two cards are an Ace and a Ten. Again suppose that you and the dealer, playing alone, each have your initial two cards and that the deck then runs out and must be shuffled before you draw. Suppose also that the dealer's up card is a Three, your hole cards total thirteen, and the count before the shuffle was (1,0,0). Why then that "other" which the dealer has must be an Eight, and he will be drawing to an initial total of eleven. Instead of a poor hand, he has a superb hand, so for this particular hand you must draw until you have seventeen or more rather than standing on the customary thirteen.

The ultimate strategy generally wins at one and a half to two times the rate of the Ten-count strategy. Furthermore, it does not lose its power as rapidly as the Ten-count strategy does under adverse situations. For example, some casinos shuffle the deck five, ten, or more cards from the end when they suspect a player is counting. This is moderately effective against the Ten-count strategy. However, the ultimate strategy finds favorable situations considerably earlier in the deck, in general, than does the Ten-count strategy.

The ultimate strategy should prove to be an increasingly important weapon as casinos attempt to take countermeasures against the growing number of system players.

The Home Game

Twenty-one is widely played, outside the casinos, in private homes throughout the world and in the Armed Forces. The variations in rules for the home game are much more numerous than those we have listed in Chapter 8. Although there are new mathematical difficulties involved, it is possible to analyze the home game using certain simple extensions of the methods we used in solving the casino game. However, the time, trouble, and expense do not seem justified in view of the fact that one can deal fairly well with most aspects of the home game by simple arguments based on what is already known about the casino game.

One key, new feature of the home game is that the deal is not fixed. Often the first dealer is chosen by dealing the cards until the first Black Jack appears. The player receiving this card becomes the dealer. When another player has a natural and the dealer does not, that player becomes the new dealer. Between hands a dealer may sell or give away his deal. Alternately, the deal may rotate after a fixed number of cards have been played. We consider this fairer. We recommend for the home game that a rotating deal and the basic rules of Chapter 3 be employed, with perhaps some of the variations of Chapter 9 included. In this case, our strategies apply unchanged.

A frequent rule in the home game is that the dealer wins ties. With this rule, the game becomes very favorable to the dealer. This unevenness makes an evening's outcome much more subject to luck and, in our opinion, spoils the game. When the dealer wins ties, the player should tend to stand more than in the casino game.

In another common home-game variation, the player is paid double for a natural. This variation helps the player by about 2.5 per cent.

The most important variation in the home game is the one which allows the dealer to draw or stand as he pleases. This is the variation which leads to considerable new mathematical complexities. For discussion and further elaboration on the home game, the reader is referred to [3].

The following discussion is for the reader with some mathematical background and interest. We will indicate how the seemingly much more complex situation involving variable rules for the dealer can be studied by the methods that were used to discover our strategies for the case of fixed rules for the dealer. That the player's strategy should, in general, shift in response to a change in the dealer's strategy, was tacitly indicated in the discussion of the soft-17 rules in Chapter 8.

One might begin by considering each up card of the dealer separately and asking the question, "What strategy should I adopt so that, when faced by best play on the part of the dealer, my advantage will be greatest?" We must be precise about what we mean by a strategy. A particularly simple choice is to define a strategy for the dealer as a pair of standing numbers, one hard and one soft, and to define a strategy for the player also as a pair of standing numbers plus doubling-down and pair-splitting information. For a first study we could fix the pair-splitting and doubling-down strategies. One could then compute the player's advantage (that is, mathematical expectation), for each fixed up card, for various dealer strategies versus player strategies. The result would be an $M \times N$ payoff matrix of the type familiar in the theory of two-person games [23,47]. There are 81 pairs of standing numbers between 12 and 21 (other choices are always relatively less profitable). However the game matrix would be much smaller than 81×81, for most of these pairs can be quickly eliminated. For example, it is never good strategy to have one's hard standing number greater than one's soft standing number. The problem should reduce to a collection of small matrices, one for each up card of the dealer. It seems intuitively probable that some of the pay-off matrices will yield mixed strategy solutions. Thus, in the best strategy for the game with dealer's variable strategy we may have a qualitively new feature for both player and dealer: the use of a set of strategies mixed randomly in suitable proportions.

10

A Challenge to the Casinos

In this chapter, we offer to play any casino that is skeptical of our winning strategies and thereby settle the doubts of the management. However, the operators of casinos are, in general, a very clever and alert group of people—they have to be to remain in business. It is therefore advisable to outline very carefully the conditions under which such a challenge game would be played, to ensure that they are not atypical. In particular, if a casino accepts our challenge, we would expect both sides to sign a mutually agreeable enforceable contract, complete with penalty clauses. A discussion follows of the main points that need attention and a sketch of some of the reasons for their inclusion.

Individual wealthy players who have mastered system play might use these ideas and suggest that their favorite casino play a private game with them in which shuffling is thorough and the anticheating provisions that we sketch are employed.

The Stakes

The minimum and maximum initial bets might be set at, say, $25 and $500, respectively. Note, however, that if a pair is split and doubling down occurs on both hands, an initial bet of $500 will grow into $2000. The game would be played in stages. Each stage would last either 10 days or until one side had lost $10,000, whichever occurred sooner. At the completion of a stage, but not before, either side could withdraw if it wished. Otherwise, a new stage would begin. Play would be greatly accelerated if we could field a team against the casino. Stages could be cut even to one day with ten players.

The intent of the "stages" idea is that the game should last long enough to guarantee the player (and the casino) the opportunity to win a worthwhile amount. Otherwise, the casino might refuse to continue playing after only a few hundred dollars in losses. This might not even cover expenses. Casinos, I am told, are classified as private clubs and may refuse to play any individual at any time. I have personally had this experience happen a number of times (see Chapter 6).

One difficulty here is that one side, losing heavily, might purposely slow down the play so as to effectively halt it as in a sitdown strike. To prevent this, we would carefully define a "day." For example, it might be defined as 500 or more hands completed within a 24-hour period. Further, play would proceed at the rate of at least five days per week and would occur in consecutive weeks. Thus a stage could drag out over no more than two weeks and would consist of at least 5,000 hands. We would stipulate that hands be played at the rate of at least 50 hands per hour and we would expect under normal conditions to actually play 100 to 150 hands per hour.

The Rules

The basic rules would be those of Chapter 3 plus any variations of Chapter 9 that are favorable to the player. (The casino might not agree that some of the variations claimed to favor the player actually do so. Then both sides could be pleased by including them.)

In addition to the basic rules, a number of auxiliary stipulations are needed. First, "shuffle up," the casino tactic of reshuffling the deck when good situations arise, should be restricted. It might be agreed upon that the casino may shuffle when there are ten or fewer unplayed cards (but not in the middle of a hand). Of course the casino might also wish to request that we give up our customary player's right to call for a reshuffle at any time. We could otherwise use this to destroy unfavorable situations whenever they arose.

A second stipulation, more important than it might seem at first glance, is that measures be taken to ensure a very thorough shuffling of the deck. It is well known that the order of a shuffled deck may be very noticeably dependent on its previous order if the shuffling is done either very poorly [9, p. 367] or very cleverly.* With regard to clever shuffling, a trick used by at least one magician whom we know consists of shuffling a deck eight times as follows. The deck is broken into two precisely equal parts. The upper part is taken in one hand and the lower part is taken in the other. Then the parts are shuffled together by alternating the cards from the

* For an analysis of surprisingly poor results of shuffling in records of extrasensory perception experiments, see W. Feller, Statistical aspects of ESP, Journal of Parapsychology, Vol. 4, pp. 271-298 (1940). You may also wish to read the article which follows, A Review of Dr. Feller's Critique, *ibid.*, pp. 299-319, by J. A. Greenwood and C. E. Stuart.

two parts, beginning by putting on the bottom the bottom card of the bottom part and ending, finally, with the top card of the top part going on the top. Although the original top and bottom cards remain on the top and bottom, respectively, the other cards all change their position. However, after this shuffle has been repeated eight times, the cards are found again in their original order.

Shuffling by machine might prove satisfactory. There also should be some reassurances (perhaps the over-all format will ensure this) against surreptitious deck stacking. A one-player game is preferable. True, it increases the count-player's rate of win, but the more important reason is to prevent the introduction of deliberate interference with the game via the medium of other players.

Anticheating Measures

The best way to avoid the temptation to cheat is to make it impossible to do so. In all fairness, protective measures should be taken to safeguard the casino as well as the player. To prevent the dealing of seconds, the deck could be placed on the table at all times and the dealer, using one hand only, could pick cards off the top one at a time. Better yet, the clear plastic shoe described in Chapter 7 should be used. Used cards could be placed in a rack off to one side so that the deck would at no time be picked up while it was a source of cards. The shuffling stipulation is intended to prevent deck-stacking. The deck could, upon request, be counted both before and afterwards in the presence of both sides to insure that cards had neither been added nor removed. All the applicable anticheating measures in Chapter 7 should be used. Further, both sides should have the right to impose further anticheating measures at any time during the match.

A number of players have attempted to cheat the casinos at blackjack (as well as at other games). Their methods fall into various categories. Some are in collusion with the dealer, who arranges that they win. The methods sketched above are intended to make this form of cheating impossible. Another method is for the player to mark the cards surreptitiously, perhaps, e.g., by bending them slightly, smudging them, or nicking their edges. One player, who was also a manufacturer of cards, offered vast quantities of specially marked cards made by his factory to a number of casinos. They were priced so low the casinos could not refuse. Indeed, they adopted these cards as standard. He was the only one who knew they were marked and, for a time, was a regular big winner. The story of this coup, and how it came to an end, is told in [31].

We shall play in such a way as to guarantee that we are not using any knowledge of the cards beyond that gained by the counting methods of earlier chapters. We shall play according to the strategies published in this book. If we select a particular strategy—say the Tens strategy—then at each step of the game our moves are determined for us in advance. Anyone who knows the strategy and sees our hand can also predict what we shall do. Thus, if we knew what the next card was and behaved differently than called for by our strategy, which we shall announce before play begins, anyone could detect this at once. To summarize, we shall play according to a fixed strategy and thus our winning can not possibly depend upon some secret scheme of specifically identifying the next card to be dealt.

Enforcement Provisions

A mutually agreeable set of cash fines, to be levied at the discretion of a supervisory committee, might be set up.

In actual practice, it is to be hoped that a considerable degree of mutual trust would soon develop and the strict format of the game could be informally relaxed by mutual consent, to be reinstituted if difficulties arose.

In the event that a legally enforceable agreement is not

possible, the power of public opinion might act as a restraint against either side violating the agreement.

We have always thought that a casino would derive so much publicity from publicly playing a fair, regulated game against a player using our system that the benefits of the publicity would more than offset the financial losses.

11

"Sporting" Propositions

One of the factors that adds to the interest of gambling are side bets as to various outcomes connected with the game. The game of craps is replete with such side bets and they are now an integral part of the game as played in the casinos. There are a number of side bets or propositions that arise naturally in connection with blackjack. Only one of these, insurance, seems to have been incorporated into the game so far.

One of the standard steps of the professional gambler is to learn a vast number of these propositions. Then, when one of them arises (or can be caused to arise) innocuously in conversation, the gambler develops a wager favorable to himself based on the proposition. For the interested reader we are going to discuss a number of propositions related to the game of blackjack. They are all based on the game as dealt from a fresh thoroughly shuffled deck. The odds shift if part of the deck has been used and some knowledge of the missing cards is available. The figures used in this discussion are based on the figures of Appendix B which is an extract from the data supplied by the computer in the complete deck case. Similar information has been obtained for all the decks listed in Table 4.1, but is not given here. It is our interest simply to illustrate how the data of Appendix B may be used to arrive at propositions concerning the game, rather than to attempt the hopeless task of exhaustively listing all conceivable propositions.

Knowledge of the material in this chapter is not essential for the use of our winning strategies but, rather, is meaningful depending on whether or not the reader is interested in making use of the propositions herein outlined (*we make no recommendations either way*). The discussion of various probabilities arising at blackjack, and the acquisition of the ability to use Appendix B should greatly increase the precision of the reader's intuitive feeling for the various aspects of the game.

Chances of Various Totals for the Dealer

Our first group of propositions is based on the probabilities of the dealer getting various totals, as listed in the table of dealer's probabilities in Appendix B (Table 1). Below each dealer's total, the table gives the probability that the dealer will achieve that total, starting with various up cards, when cards are dealt from a full deck. The final row in the table, labeled "over-all probability" is the probability that the dealer will achieve various totals before any cards have been dealt. Sample propositions based on the table follow.

If the player starts with a total of 18, is he, over all, more likely to win or lose? The chance that he will lose is the sum of the probabilities that the dealer will have a better total, namely 19, 20, 21, or a natural. Using the last line of Table 1, Appendix B, we add the over-all probabilities for these figures and get 0.4325. The chance that the player wins is the sum of the probabilities that the dealer has a poorer total, namely, 17 or busts; the corresponding probability figure is 0.4294. The player who bets his money on a total of 18 therefore has a very slight edge, 0.0031 or 0.31 per cent. Notice that when the dealer shows a Six, the player's chance to win, holding a total of seventeen, is 0.4208. His chance of losing is 0.4122. Thus the player who wagers that seventeen will win against a Six has an edge of 0.86 per cent. The player's advantage, when standing on various totals against individual up cards, as listed in Table 3, Appendix B, has been computed from Table 1, Appendix B, in precisely this manner. The discrepancy between our figure of 0.86 per cent, computed above for seventeen against a Six, and 0.9 per cent (0.009) given in Table 3, Appendix B, is only the result of the fact that the latter figure has been rounded off, a minor fact of no particular significance.

The figures in Table 3, Appendix B are based on the assumption the dealer has no natural. However, if an Ace or Ten is showing, there is a second group of propositions that are possible before the dealer checks to see if he has a natural. They are not listed in Table 3. If the dealer has not yet checked to see if he has a natural, the corresponding calculations are made much in the same way as before, except that the probability of the dealer having a natural should be added to the player's chance to lose (we assume the player has no natural; the proposition in that case would not be very interesting). For example, Table 1, Appendix B, shows that nineteen loses against a Ten, 0.4438 of the time and wins, 0.4416 of the time. Thus, the player who wagers that nineteen will win under these conditions is at a disadvantage of 0.2 per cent, whereas Table 3, Appendix B, shows us that he has an 8.3 per cent advantage if the dealer checks and finds he has no natural.

It may be a little surprising how sharply the situation

changes when the dealer shows a Nine instead of a Ten. Nineteen against a Nine wins 0.4593 of the time and loses only 0.1834 of the time; thus it will win, instead of lose, with odds of slightly better than 5 to 2.

One must be careful to say what one means in wording propositions of this sort. For example, to wager (even money) that nineteen will win against a Nine, instead of losing *or* tying, is a poor bet for 19 wins only 0.4593 of the time, or less than half of the time.

Another kind of insurance that the casinos might offer is insurance to protect the player against the dealer *not* busting. The dealer busts a little less than two times in seven, according to Table 1 (Appendix B), so a payoff of 1 to 3 would favor the casino by about 5 per cent. If the dealer busts, the player loses his insurance bet. If the dealer does not bust, the player wins one third the amount of his insurance.

A player who wagers $2 to $7 that the dealer busts has a 0.7 per cent edge.

An even money bet is perhaps simpler to consider. The chance of the dealer not busting is about 0.7164 on any one hand. It follows that the chance the dealer does not bust on either of two consecutive hands is about $0.7164 \times 0.7164 = 0.513$. It is therefore a good (2.6 per cent edge) even-money bet to wager that the dealer does not bust on two consecutive hands.

Chances of Winning When Starting with Various Hole Cards

Another large group of propositions can be based on whether a given pair of hole cards will become a winning hand or not. For this we refer to Table 4, Appendix B. The general rule is quite simple. If your hole cards do not form a pair that should be split, then you have the advantage facing a dealer's given up card and using the basic strategy, if, and only if, your advantage as listed in the drawing and standing part of Table 4 is positive. For a pair that should be split, you have the advantage if, and only if, your advantage in the pair-splitting part of the table is positive. For example, when the dealer has a Ten showing, the player has the advantage (we are always assuming, of course, that there is no knowledge of the dealer's hole card available yet other than the fact that he does not have a natural) if, and only if, his hole cards total 10, 11, 19, 20, or 21 or if they are a pair of Aces. Recall that both Aces and Eights should be split against a Ten. However only with split Aces does the player get an advantage. In the instance of split Eights, he only diminishes his disadvantage slightly.

The doubling-down section of Table 4 may be disregarded in determining whether the player has the advantage with a given pair of hole cards. This may be seen as follows. If the player has the advantage when he doubles down on two given hole cards, he must also have it if he draws or stands. For in doubling down he gives up the freedom of drawing more than one additional card. Thus, the chance that he wins is less than if he followed the best drawing or standing strategy. Thus, if drawing and standing were disadvantageous, doubling down would be more so (the player gets, on the average poorer hands and has more money wagered on them) and would not be recommended.

If the precise advantage (when the basic strategy is used) for a given two hole cards is sought, simply consult the entry in the table corresponding to the procedure recommended by the basic strategy. Here the doubling-down table will also be of use. For example, holding (*5,6*) against a Ten, the recommended procedure is to double down. The advantage given is 20.2 per cent. This leads us to a fine point. For certain mathematical reasons, it was desirable to measure the player's advantage (as used in this book the term advantage is intended to be a colloquial synonym for the term "mathematical expectation" [9]) in terms of the *original* (one unit) bet made by the player. Thus to *say* that the player's advantage when doubling down with (*5,6*) against a dealer's up card of Ten is 20.2 per cent means that, on the average over many recurrences of this situation, the player will win 20.2 per cent of his *original* bet. However, since his bet is double his original bet, the excess of winning hands over losing hands is only 10.1 per cent. Note also that the player who draws and stands with (*5,6*) against a Ten has an excess of wins over losses of 12.1 per cent. This figure is larger than the 10.1 per cent figure for doubling down, as should be expected from the previously noted fact that doubling down produces, on the average, poorer hands than standing or drawing. In fact, if d_{ij} is the player's advantage when doubling down on holding hole cards (i,j) and if s_{ij} is the player's corresponding advantage when drawing or standing on those same hole cards (both as given in Table 4, Appendix B), then $d_{ij}/2$ is the excess of wins over losses when doubling down. Then $d_{ij}/2 \leqslant s_{ij}$ always and the basic strategy recommends doubling down if, and only if, $d_{ij} > s_{ij}$.

Chances of Tying the Dealer

The chances that the dealer and the player will tie, or "push," depend on the strategy that is being used by the player. For example, the player can stand whenever he has 16 or less. If he happens to receive a hard total of 17 or more, he can draw until he busts. If he receives a soft total of 17 or more he can draw until it changes to a hard total and then apply his hard strategy. It is evident that a player who follows this strategy will never tie the dealer.

Near the other extreme is the player who imitates the dealer's strategy. The chances of a tie between this player and the dealer are easily calculated from the last row of Table 1, Appendix B. The chance of both the dealer and this player holding 17 is 0.1458 × 0.1458, or 0.0213. Calculating in a similar manner for totals of 18, 19, 20, 21, and a natural, and then adding them, we find the chances of a tie to be 0.0972. It can be shown by simple arguments that the best hard standing number for the production of ties is 17, the same as the dealer's. It is also easy to show that the best soft-standing number is at least 17. It would not be too difficult to determine whether 17 itself is the best soft standing number. It either is or it gives results that are extremely close to the best. Therefore we shall leave it at that for now and simply say that the strategy of imitating the dealer either produces the greatest likelihood of a tie or comes very close to doing so. Thus under no strategy is the probability of a tie greater than 0.0972 plus some very small number.

The probability of the occurrence of a tie between the dealer and a player using the basic strategy also can be calculated. However, since we have access to good experimental figures, we will simply quote these. Dr. Allan Wilson, in playing 304,566 hands on a computer using the basic strategy (except that doubling down after pair splitting was not included—a negligible error for our purposes), found the probability of the occurrence of a tie to be a little less than 0.0911 (with a standard deviation of 0.0005).

12

The Future of the Game

The appearance of numerous system players will ultimately necessitate important changes in the game of twenty-one as it is now played. We can gain some first insights into these changes by discussing the means through which the Nevada casinos have dealt with the handful of successful players (whom we refer to as "count" players because they counted cards) that have emerged in that state during the last decade. Most of the stories surrounding these early players are not a matter of public record or are even known beyond a small circle of acquaintances. No part of the legend became known to me until sometime after I had completed the winning strategy outlined in this book and had arrived in Nevada to test it in actual play.

Early Winning Players

The first of the successful system players, a much different personality than the others in the group and in no way representative, was a colorful individual known as "Greasy John." Large and obese, he acquired his name from his habit of coming to the casino with a large bag of very greasy fried chicken. He played for as long as twenty hours at a stretch, never leaving the table. The casino supplied the drinks and innumerable meals of varying sizes could always be drawn from the huge bag of chicken. It soon became apparent that "Greasy John" wanted to play alone. As crowded as the casinos are, once he became a familiar face, he did not have much trouble keeping other players away. His profanity and drinking drove off all but the hardiest of women players and finally the casinos forbade all women to play at the same table with him.

Since Greasy John's hands were generally dripping with chicken fat, the cards soon became too oily to handle comfortably. Even though decks were changed frequently, the grease was sufficient to drive away the men players.

Greasy John played for long hours day after day, and in a few months, became wealthy enough to retire. He suffered a heart attack and died shortly afterwards. We have no knowledge of the system that Greasy John used; the surviving details are inadequate for a sure deduction. However, it seems most probable that he employed end play. As noted in an earlier chapter, end play will produce astronomical gains in a short time in spite of the fact that the player's basic playing strategy is poor. Furthermore, end play is a very natural idea, easy to verify empirically, and probably has occurred to a great many players.

For those players who follow "System Smitty," we have, in most cases, omitted the details of the colorful backgrounds of the individuals involved, and those parts of their adventures which might serve to identify them. We also have regretfully omitted those human interest portions of the legend involving areas such as sex, vice, "con men," and the mob. We must further emphasize that the legend is a composite of many separate stories told to me by different people. However, for the most part the stories are mutually consistent and the people telling them were direct participants. Therefore, I believe the story is substantially accurate.

To my knowledge, the first person who employed a "count" system in successful casino play was Benjamin F. ("System Smitty") Smith, a well-known figure in the Las Vegas casinos [1]. According to Mr. Z., a mutual acquaintance who has seen Smitty's voluminous notebooks, Smitty spent several years playing out 100,000 hands, in an effort to determine the proper standing numbers when a Ten-count was employed. The system, as related to me by Mr. Z., gave a fair approximation as to where to stand for various values of the ratio Tens/others. However, there were certain moderate errors, which resulted, at least partly, from the nature of the system.

That the errors were unavoidable consequences of the system's format can perhaps best be explained by referring to the standing numbers part of Table 5.3. Smitty's system in effect assigned a single value of the ratio to each of the hard standing number squares along certain parallel diagonals. Suppose, for example, that the numbers 3.9 in (16,2), (3.7) in (15,3), (3.3) in (14,4), 3.0 in (13.5), and (2.3) in (12,6) were all replaced by a single number, say 3. Notice that no single number can possibly agree with more than one of the entries on this diagonal, since they are all distinct. The same is true for the other long, parallel diagonals.

Smitty's system replaced the standing numbers by the following mnemonic device. Along the diagonal described above, the sum of the cards in the player's hand and the dealer's up card is always eighteen. For all such situations, termed "of eighteen type," there is but a single ratio value, say 3. If the ratio exceeded 3, one drew; if not, one stood.

Using Table 5.3, and taking averages along appropriate diagonals (all diagonals are broken off at column six—

column seven is the dividing line), we can construct a similar mnemonic for standing numbers. It is given in Table 12.1.

TABLE 12.1. *Hard Standing Numbers Corresponding to the Ten-Count Strategy, Assuming a Running Count Is Kept of the Ratio of Others to Tens, When Situations Are Classified According to "Type."* *

Situation type	Stand only if ratio is given
14	2.0
15	2.2
16	2.5
17	2.8
18	3.2
19	3.9
20	4.5
21	5.6
22	4.6
23	1.2
24	1.4
25	1.8
26	2.3

* The Ace column is not included. Up cards of *2* through *6* and *7* through *10* are grouped separately.

In addition to the moderate errors in standing numbers that were a necessary part of System Smitty's method, there was no detailed strategy for doubling down and for pair splitting. These factors, in toto, probably cut two or three per cent off the player's advantage, not to mention the increased rate of attrition of the small "waiting" bets. Since the bulk of the favorable bets are in the 0 to 3 per cent range, the player's rate of win is greatly diminished over that cited in Chapter 5. The only alternative for the player who wants to make a big win is to overbet his capital (in the sense of the theory of proportional or "fixed fraction" betting [18]), greatly increasing the chance of ruin, and hope for the best.

Smitty probably did precisely this, for he has had many spectacular win-loss sequences. Mr. Z. said he was present one night when Smitty won $108,000 at the blackjack tables (that is a considerable sum with a $500 limit) and lost it all back by the next morning. He did not even have the price of breakfast left.

Smitty's system, which was first used in the mid-50's I believe, seems to have spread to a small group of players including a certain old-time gambler whom we shall call Mr. F., Mr. F's mistress,* the Mr. X of Chapter 6, Mr. Z, the little dark-haired guy mentioned previously, and a young player commonly known both as Junior and as "Sonny."

This group of players pumped out large sums of money from the blackjack tables within the next few years. There is no way to determine exactly how large the sums were. For what it is worth, the "grapevine" credits Mr. F. with $50,000 gross winnings, Mr. Z. with $56,000 gross (afterwards divided with his bankrollers), and Mr. X. with $100,000 to $150,000 gross. The little dark-haired guy is supposed to have cleared $250,000.

In any case, the members of the group won large amounts in short times in only a few casinos, and as a consequence the casinos, initially skeptical of the possibility that the game could be beaten, finally barred each of the members of the group from play at the Twenty-One tables and spread the warning to their colleagues.

Casino Countermeasures to Count Players

During and after this period a number of casino responses and countermeasures to count players either came into existence or developed further.

Cheating. Cheating has been connected with card games for centuries and will continue for a long time to

* The story of this woman's life would itself fill a book.

come. The only defense against this countermeasure seems to be to play only at honest casinos and to put pressure on the casinos that cheat, through such means as publicity and regulatory agencies, if possible. Cheating is the principal danger for the would-be system player. It can fool him into thinking that the system does not work.

Barring. A casino can exclude a small class of players without difficulty. However, it does not seem feasible on a large scale. With the early system players, photographs could be distributed to all local casinos but for thousands of players, this idea is simply impractical. Along these same lines, even though a given casino's employees may remember a particular individual and bar him from further play, barring is not a defense for the casinos as a whole because it is possible that the individual may work his way through the hundreds of existing casinos and allay suspicion by winning only a few hundred dollars at each one.

It is obvious that casino employees are trained to remember people. Junior (also called "Sonny") told me that, on one occasion, after he was universally barred in the casinos, he went to the make-up department of one of the Hollywood movie studios. He paid $500 for a complete disguise. On the basis of his facial structure, color, and build they decided to disguise him as a middle-aged Chinese. The disguise even included a carapace to be fitted over his torso. He tried out his nice new outfit one evening in a casino in which there were six employees on duty who knew him. Five of them paid no attention to him. Shortly after he began play the sixth employee wandered over from the bar, spotted him at once and exclaimed, "Hey, look everybody. There's Sonny all dressed up like a Chinese." Junior still keeps his beloved Chinese outfit stored away somewhere, buried under years of accumulated dust.

Shuffle up. Shuffle up is another casino strategy which is effective against a small class of players, but which has a serious draw-back when system players become numerous. It costs the casinos money by slowing down the game and it also alienates some customers. Further, shuffle up is fraught with difficulties for the casino. How does a dealer know when he is facing a system player and when he is not? The best count players can play faster than any dealer can deal, or smoother and more effortlessly than most players. Thus they have ample freedom to adopt a guise. And there are many subtle ways to camouflage one's bet size variation (the variation can, when need be, be made quite small, even 2 to 1 or less).

Here is a casino pitfall. Suppose a dealer shuffles according to some simple rule like that which requires that he shuffle every time the player increases his bet (more generally, alters his behavior pattern). The player who is aware of this is then effectively in control of the shuffle, can cause it to come at exactly those times that he desires it, and can use it as follows. At the beginning of a fresh deck the player can make a *big* bet. If the deck goes bad, he can make a *bigger* bet and cause a shuffle. After the casino shuffles, but before a card is dealt, he then reduces his bet from bigger to big. If the deck stays average or gets good, the player continues with big bets. The results will be that all bets will be a constant big size and that the dealer will obligingly shuffle away all bad situations. Thus the typical situation will be quite good and the player will win at a rapid rate. Regrettably, this idea did not occur to me until after a perfect situation for its application (p. 112) has passed.

A shuffle up half-way through the deck was generally enough to stop all the early (1950's) count players. However, our Ten-count strategy finds winning situations after only a few cards have been dealt. The ultimate strategy is even better; it finds winning situations after only one card has been dealt (or burned or seen on the bottom).

It is even possible to sit at the left of a table full of

players and get enough information from the cards of theirs that are exposed to then introduce variations to the basic strategy which result in gains large enough to give the player a slight edge on the first round of play. Shuffle up has no effect on advantages in the first round of play.

Rules Changes

Perhaps the most interesting factor affecting the future of the game is the possibility of rules changes. Changes that seem to have come about over the last decade—probably arising in part, because of the exploits of the early count players—are a gradual spread of the soft-seventeen rule and of restrictions on doubling down and pair splitting.

The casinos have certain problems associated with rules changes. First, they will be unpopular with some players who are otherwise unaware. Secondly, there is enough information in Chapter 8 so that players, whether or not they follow a system, can choose to play in those casinos whose rules give them a better break.

Furthermore, if players tend to lose more often the game may decrease in popularity. If in turn, this causes the casinos to make the rules more unfavorable in an effort to gain back revenue, the resulting feedback could destroy the game. Because of the significant occurrence of very favorable situations of 5 to 10 per cent or more, the rules alterations against the players will have to be quite large to stop the effectiveness of system play. The effect on the nonsystem players might be ruinous.

On the other hand, players may continue to play against the poorer odds: many players continue to gamble even in games with terribly unfavorable odds, such as most slot machines, keno, chuck-a-luck, and some of the side bets in craps. Of course, with the possible exception of a couple of the craps bets, these situations are not equivalent to the case of bad bets in blackjack because in the former, one generally loses small amounts steadily while awaiting a gigantic win, and in the latter, one is steadily ground down during a series of even-money bets. The psychology of the two situations is much different.

If nonsystem players tend to persevere against worsening odds, things might temporarily stabilize with the nonsystem players losing more than they used to and the system players winning consistently. This equilibrium would eventually be destroyed, however, by a steady increase in the percentage of players using our system.

The End of Blackjack?

Whether the game as played in honest casinos will ultimately cease to exist altogether or whether there will be a transformation in the rules until they are much different than the present rules, we hesitate to guess. In the short run, over the next few years, we predict that the incidence of cheating will gradually increase and that the rules will gradually get less favorable. Attempts at shuffle up will be partly successful at first but will finally be abandoned as the number of system players increase. The system players who make large wins in a given casino may be barred from further play in an entire locality. However, many players will win only a few hundred dollars per casino and will, at the completion of their "route" have large accumulated winnings. Whether cheating or worsening rules finally becomes the dominant development will depend on local conditions such as the existence and power of regulatory agencies and the general level of awareness among the players of the methods of cheating.

It is possible to build miniature low-cost readily concealed mechanical or electronic devices on which the player can count the cards simply by typing them in with his finger as they are seen. If these devices are manufactured and sold in quantity, they will allow anyone to play the ultimate strategy without effort. They will complete the revolutionizing of the game that has been launched by our publication of winning strategies.

The probable large effect on the game of blackjack which will probably result from our modest scientific investigation brings to mind the question: Will the rapid development of modern science and technology continue to produce winning systems for various gambling games?

Science and Gambling

The mathematical theory of probability originated in the sixteenth and seventeenth centuries with the consideration by Cardano, Pascal, and others of various gambling games, and with their investigation as to whether or not there were systems for beating them. Most notably, these games were the forerunners and relatives of craps. From that time until the recent past, a series of persons whose names are illustrious in mathematics and physics have seriously thought about gambling games (and have often made important related contributions to the mathematical theory of probability!). In addition to Cardano and Pascal, some earlier examples are Fermat, James and Daniel Bernouilli, Laplace, and Poisson.

At the turn of this century, the great mathematician and physicist, Henri Poincaré, considered the possibility of predicting the outcome of a trial of roulette by physical, rather than mathematical, methods. He concluded that this was impossible via an argument based on the mathematical concept of a continuous function. However, the concepts involved illustrated certain philosophical concepts in science (see [30], pages 69-70 and pages 76-77). Also early in this century the great English statistician Karl Pearson spent many years analyzing the records of certain roulette wheels. However, for more than forty years there seem to have been no successful scientifically based attempts to devise winning gambling systems.

The modern high-speed computer, essential to a careful analysis of blackjack, has been widely available only for the last five or ten years; without the help of such a computer the analysis which led to this book would have been impossible.* With the very rapid, continuing increase in the number of scientists and engineers, and the rise of fantastic new scientific tools, the interest in the possibility of winning gambling systems is increasing.

We predict that scientifically based winning systems for other games will appear over the years, probably more and more frequently, and that the casinos will ultimately be forced to supplement their traditional reliance on an empirical cunning by "fighting science with science."

* The IBM 704 high-speed computer which we used, spent about three hours calculating. It calculates many millions of times as fast as a human, and is nearly error-free. It would have taken roughly ten thousand man-years to do the same calculations with the aid of a desk calculator.

APPENDIX A

Table of Random Digits*

11 16 43 63 18	75 06 13 76 74	40 60 31 61 52	83 23 53 73 61
21 21 59 17 91	76 83 15 86 78	40 94 15 35 85	69 95 86 09 16
10 43 84 44 82	66 55 83 76 49	73 50 58 34 72	55 95 31 79 57
36 79 22 62 36	33 26 66 65 83	39 41 21 60 13	11 44 28 93 20
73 94 40 47 73	12 03 25 14 14	57 99 47 67 48	54 62 74 85 11
49 56 31 28 72	14 06 39 31 04	61 83 45 91 99	15 46 98 22 85
64 20 84 82 37	41 70 17 31 17	91 40 27 72 27	79 51 62 10 07
51 48 67 28 75	38 60 52 93 41	58 29 98 38 80	20 12 51 07 94
99 75 62 63 60	64 51 61 79 71	40 68 49 99 48	33 88 07 64 13
71 32 55 52 17	13 01 57 29 07	75 97 86 42 98	08 07 46 20 55
65 28 59 71 98	12 13 85 30 10	34 55 63 98 61	88 26 77 60 68
17 26 45 73 27	38 22 42 93 01	65 99 05 70 48	25 06 77 75 71
95 63 99 97 54	31 19 99 25 58	16 38 11 50 69	25 41 68 78 75
61 55 57 64 04	86 21 01 18 08	52 45 88 88 80	78 35 26 79 13
78 13 79 87 68	04 68 98 71 30	33 00 78 56 07	92 00 84 48 97
62 49 09 92 15	84 98 72 87 59	38 71 23 15 12	08 58 86 14 90
24 21 66 34 44	21 28 30 70 44	58 72 20 36 78	19 18 66 96 02
16 97 59 54 28	33 22 65 59 03	26 18 86 94 97	51 35 14 77 99
59 13 83 95 42	71 16 85 76 09	12 89 35 40 48	07 25 58 61 49
29 47 85 96 52	50 41 43 19 66	33 18 68 13 46	85 09 53 72 82
96 15 59 50 09	27 42 97 29 18	79 89 32 94 48	88 39 25 42 11
29 62 16 65 83	62 96 61 24 68	48 44 91 51 02	44 12 61 94 38
12 63 97 52 91	71 02 01 72 65	94 20 50 42 59	68 98 35 05 61
14 54 43 71 34	54 71 40 24 01	38 64 80 92 78	81 31 37 74 00
83 40 38 88 27	09 83 41 13 33	04 29 24 60 28	75 66 62 69 54
67 64 20 52 04	30 69 74 48 06	17 02 64 97 37	85 87 51 21 39
64 04 19 90 11	61 04 02 73 09	48 07 07 68 48	02 53 19 77 37
17 04 89 45 23	97 44 45 99 04	30 15 99 54 50	83 77 84 61 15
93 03 98 94 16	52 79 51 06 31	12 14 89 22 31	31 36 16 06 50
82 24 43 43 92	96 60 71 72 20	73 83 87 70 67	24 86 39 75 76
96 99 05 52 44	70 69 32 52 55	73 54 74 37 59	95 63 23 95 55
09 11 97 48 03	97 30 38 87 01	07 27 79 32 17	79 42 12 17 69
57 66 64 12 04	47 58 97 83 64	65 12 84 83 34	07 49 32 80 98
46 49 26 15 94	26 72 95 82 72	38 71 66 13 80	60 21 20 50 99
08 43 31 91 72	08 32 02 08 39	31 92 17 64 58	73 72 00 86 57
10 01 17 50 04	86 05 44 11 90	57 23 82 74 64	61 48 75 23 29
92 42 06 54 31	16 53 00 55 47	24 21 94 10 90	08 53 16 15 78
35 54 25 58 65	07 30 44 70 10	31 30 94 93 87	02 33 00 24 76
86 59 52 62 47	18 55 22 94 91	20 75 09 70 24	72 61 96 66 28
72 11 53 49 85	58 03 69 91 37	28 53 78 43 95	26 65 43 78 51

* This table appears through the courtesy of The RAND Corporation and the McGraw-Hill Book Company, Inc. and is reprinted by permission from The Compleat Strategyst, by J. D. Williams, pp. 219-221 [44].

07	42	85	88	63	96	02	38	89	36	97	92	94	12	20	86	43	19	44	85
35	37	92	79	22	28	90	65	50	13	40	56	83	32	22	40	48	69	11	22
10	98	22	28	07	10	92	02	62	99	41	48	39	29	35	17	06	17	82	52
90	12	73	33	41	77	80	61	24	46	93	04	06	64	76	24	99	04	10	99
63	00	21	29	90	23	51	06	87	74	76	86	93	93	00	84	97	80	75	04
40	77	98	63	82	48	45	46	52	69	02	98	25	79	91	50	76	59	19	30
43	21	61	26	08	18	16	78	46	31	94	47	97	65	00	39	17	00	66	29
96	16	76	43	75	74	10	89	36	43	52	29	17	58	22	95	96	69	09	47
70	97	56	26	93	35	68	47	26	07	03	68	40	36	00	52	83	15	53	81
85	81	26	18	75	23	57	07	57	54	58	93	92	83	66	86	76	56	74	65

37	10	06	24	92	63	64	24	76	38	54	72	35	65	27	53	07	63	82	35
53	40	61	38	55	38	51	92	95	00	84	82	88	12	48	25	54	83	40	75
55	17	28	15	56	18	85	65	90	43	65	79	90	19	14	81	36	30	51	73
40	35	38	48	07	47	76	74	68	90	87	91	73	85	49	48	21	37	17	08
18	89	90	96	12	77	54	15	76	75	26	90	78	81	73	71	18	92	83	77
68	14	12	53	40	92	55	11	13	26	68	05	26	54	22	88	46	00	63	52
51	55	99	11	59	81	31	06	32	51	42	58	76	81	49	88	14	79	97	00
92	21	43	33	86	73	45	97	93	59	97	17	65	54	16	67	64	20	50	51
15	08	95	05	57	33	16	68	70	94	53	29	58	71	33	38	26	49	47	08
96	46	10	06	04	11	12	02	22	54	23	01	19	41	08	29	19	66	51	87

28	17	74	41	11	15	70	57	38	35	75	76	84	95	49	24	54	36	32	85
66	95	34	47	37	81	12	70	74	93	86	66	87	03	41	66	46	07	56	48
19	71	22	72	63	84	57	54	98	20	56	72	77	20	36	50	34	73	35	21
68	75	66	47	57	19	98	79	22	22	27	93	67	80	10	09	61	70	44	08
75	02	26	53	32	98	60	62	94	51	31	99	46	90	72	37	35	49	30	25
11	32	37	00	69	90	26	98	92	66	02	98	59	53	03	15	18	25	01	66
55	20	86	34	70	18	15	82	52	83	89	96	51	02	06	95	83	09	54	06
11	47	40	87	86	05	59	46	70	45	45	58	72	96	11	98	57	94	24	81
81	42	28	68	42	60	99	77	96	69	01	07	10	85	30	74	30	57	75	09
21	77	17	59	63	23	15	19	02	74	90	20	96	85	21	14	29	33	91	94

42	27	81	21	60	32	57	61	42	78	04	98	26	84	70	27	87	51	54	80
17	69	76	01	14	63	24	73	20	96	19	74	02	46	37	97	37	73	21	12
05	68	63	02	43	34	13	40	29	36	50	19	77	98	69	86	49	76	87	09
52	99	24	66	50	89	91	05	73	95	46	95	46	75	36	28	96	88	19	36
94	51	89	39	84	81	47	86	77	50	82	54	96	26	76	31	12	34	98	99
00	18	47	21	86	78	90	67	54	80	61	79	88	16	00	80	01	88	47	42
87	46	26	31	65	79	81	66	16	30	57	66	62	90	55	46	51	80	14	87
88	69	25	87	16	12	27	34	81	76	29	80	56	49	94	66	87	26	22	30
20	09	44	29	62	41	38	21	67	68	06	71	13	49	39	19	59	97	62	47
60	93	58	15	04	50	52	08	21	53	13	93	44	68	85	58	31	58	83	66

51	39	28	59	36	43	89	85	05	96	28	54	99	83	27	99	94	32	53	77
54	23	94	19	18	79	52	64	62	74	40	87	16	18	03	25	76	75	54	84
57	89	27	33	94	07	16	09	02	62	47	70	43	83	55	71	70	88	01	17
02	33	07	47	36	53	27	44	44	68	62	61	11	96	98	09	30	42	92	65
76	11	52	92	47	55	34	25	12	99	03	04	78	39	81	11	91	60	92	67
63	31	28	18	86	29	08	52	01	01	26	46	05	05	01	31	73	11	89	38
27	63	22	15	70	34	27	45	64	26	01	76	42	59	59	69	29	38	98	75
06	33	56	21	11	44	01	45	25	67	11	76	25	48	06	02	65	15	29	12
64	14	28	76	76	21	35	88	87	73	31	73	63	16	95	11	52	36	42	13
28	43	62	54	68	75	23	57	53	70	97	15	54	87	06	52	23	92	18	31

09	52	28	38	55	85	97	31	58	88	31	18	14	96	72	17	23	70	40	24
93	71	41	54	14	93	71	20	27	42	32	11	58	26	83	67	18	28	90	30
15	68	15	35	99	58	18	57	38	40	07	06	87	59	47	71	74	36	92	85
77	71	22	39	14	08	90	74	37	68	26	62	27	41	84	75	16	69	67	48
78	45	35	48	44	61	50	90	12	45	02	80	55	26	76	22	51	94	78	48
24	86	06	82	84	19	36	72	90	73	32	30	15	87	01	04	19	33	01	42
37	28	40	68	44	78	88	75	72	76	26	33	95	69	09	39	33	14	21	01
35	48	85	24	73	37	63	43	25	69	95	27	40	95	08	81	01	24	24	13
51	59	55	99	09	35	22	34	49	91	24	27	53	96	32	09	77	79	88	00
90	66	03	51	71	30	02	19	11	20	36	11	64	21	28	65	40	19	41	99

47	50	50	20	08	20	30	08	71	88	96	19	50	70	59	13	26	63	13	89
13	35	00	84	14	64	04	99	43	77	22	40	89	49	58	19	09	55	80	35
33	00	69	26	90	69	24	89	74	43	53	89	62	35	08	16	22	75	69	29
55	21	66	38	86	06	80	41	18	61	22	56	50	24	75	00	25	87	90	18
21	99	12	62	28	14	80	11	91	92	49	43	82	07	72	60	84	66	97	32
71	02	52	82	12	10	47	42	75	22	65	62	03	46	84	00	21	00	48	63
65	52	21	52	42	84	55	47	45	60	20	24	62	69	41	41	29	80	47	63
27	97	55	49	23	90	65	00	61	70	09	43	30	91	67	35	16	63	27	31
07	30	00	97	04	36	09	96	15	77	95	55	27	34	56	16	57	88	81	40
54	35	71	36	89	19	56	90	38	14	76	05	30	51	50	69	12	56	94	42

00	97	70	44	81	42	04	40	86	49	34	82	23	58	43	78	46	88	23	80
13	92	07	87	61	12	31	19	28	08	07	75	30	40	73	58	52	08	00	22
08	39	53	70	43	37	88	03	41	72	04	20	49	44	34	62	79	88	19	02
46	16	66	72	06	01	61	94	37	69	96	77	01	94	40	29	70	04	20	93
87	76	77	76	07	03	74	20	16	13	65	98	96	28	43	10	91	73	44	58
29	88	09	52	88	21	64	44	65	87	06	64	49	47	84	66	99	56	18	12
36	24	83	66	66	14	89	45	92	73	88	95	04	60	77	34	65	11	20	38
12	38	62	96	56	30	47	42	59	64	21	48	29	54	22	02	00	23	36	71
52	06	87	38	01	52	18	81	94	91	55	13	76	10	39	02	00	66	99	13
41	72	75	21	71	56	71	90	60	54	98	44	18	15	29	59	60	76	52	25

APPENDIX B

Basic Probabilities for the Complete Deck

An understanding of Chapter 11 and of this appendix are not essential to the rest of the book. They have been included because they may be of interest to mathematically inclined readers.

The tables which are given in this appendix are an extract of the computer's results for the case of cards being dealt from one complete deck. It is results like these, including one full set for each of the decks described in Table 4.1, that were used to construct the theory of the game which is given in this book. Because of the extreme length of the data —there are enough final results alone to fill an entire book the size of this one with numbers—we necessarily limit ourselves to presenting the complete deck figures. Furthermore, we present only an extract of the complete-deck figures.

For those interested in such matters, the computation was done to eight decimal places and then rounded off to five decimal places before being printed out. Since in our discussion and application of these figures we generally only need three decimal places, the tables given here usually are to three decimal places.

All figures are to be understood as having a decimal point on the left, even though the decimal point is omitted. For example, —039 is to be read as —0.039.

We emphasize again that figures in this appendix were computed assuming one complete deck and the rules of Chapter 3, including the rule of a dealer's soft standing number of seventeen. Inasmuch as the figures may vary considerably if these conditions are altered, any deductions that one might make which are based on this appendix are precisely applicable only to the situation just described. Such deductions do, however, give rough insight into situations in which there are several decks in play or in which the rules are different.

I have made one fundamental simplification in our calculations which leads to certain small errors throughout the work. The following discussion will show that these errors are small, that they introduce no significant errors into the strategies, and most important, that the figures for the player's overall advantage are better than I say they are. Some of this was mentioned previously in a footnote at the beginning of Chapter 3.

The fundamental simplification is this. In all the calculations, the effect of the cards the *player* draws was neglected. For example in Table 1 the dealer's probabilities are based on a full deck except for his up card. Then Tables 2a and 2b were deduced from Table 1, given that the player had various totals and that he was drawing from a deck which had only the dealer's up card missing.

In reality, of course, certain cards were removed from the deck to form the player's total. These missing cards affect the calculations in two ways. First, they affect the dealer's true probabilities. Secondly, they affect the player's probabilities of various totals when he draws. The exact method of doing the calculation would have been to combine a weighted average of probabilities, computed for each of the many ways through which a given pair of hands (dealer's and player's) can occur. Because this calculation is far beyond the capacity of any existing computer or of any computer that will be available in the near future, we were forced to make some simplifying assumption.

The question then is what sort of errors are thereby introduced? The following arguments indicate that the various errors introduced tend largely to average out. First, the dealer's probabilities, while not the dealer's true probabilities for any specific player's hand, are quite close to the true ones. Furthermore, they are very close to the properly weighted average of the various, true dealer's probabilities. This also happens for the effects on the probabilities of various totals when the player draws to a certain total. Roughly speaking, the small residual error that does not cancel out occurs because our assumption makes the deck appear to have more small cards than it really does. To illustrate, when small cards predominate in making up a player's total, the deck he is considering drawing from, and that has supplied the dealer's hole card, is shifted more towards a "high-card-rich" deck than the deck is shifted towards a "low-card-rich" deck by a predominance of high cards in the player's hand. This is simply because fewer high cards than low cards are required to add to a specified total. A deck with an excess of low cards tends to hurt the player. Thus the effect should be that our calculations give figures for the player's advantage that are less favorable than the true expectation.

This effect has received two independent confirmations. First, as remarked in a footnote to Chapter 3, Dr. Allan Wilson's results from playing 300,000 hands of blackjack on a computer with the basic strategy and typical rules, show the player's advantage is + 0.16 per cent ± 0.07 per cent (sigma, the standard deviation, is 0.10 per cent). Thus the correction to our figure of −0.21 per cent is about 0.37 per cent in favor of the player. Secondly, the assumptions of the Baldwin calculation tend to make the deck seem to have an even greater excess of low cards. Thus our arguments suggest that their figure for the player's advantage should be more pessimistic than ours. It is; their result is −0.62 per cent.*

In the determination of the player's strategy, the errors in our figures may cause errors in strategy but only when the decision is, percentage wise, very close. But then the errors caused by the erroneous strategy are very small. This, plus the low frequency of close decisions, means the effect of any strategic errors of this type on the player's advantage are also very small. This shows a virtue of the running count. Roughly speaking, in certain close decisions such as whether or not to draw on hard sixteen when the dealer holds a Ten, the decision will depend on what cards the player has drawn to make up his total of 16. For example, it is known that, holding (*10,4,2*) the player should stand while holding (*10,6*) he should draw. If several small cards have been drawn to make the total of sixteen, the decision may be fairly clear cut. For example, if the cards drawn were (*4,4, 4,4*), the player's *disadvantage* in drawing to hard 16 against a Ten is *precisely* (!) 6.267 per cent, as compared with the average player advantage of 0.8 per cent in drawing to hard 16 against a ten.

One might attempt to improve the basic strategy by calculating, for each combination of cards that the player can draw to make a total of hard 16, the advantage or disadvantage of standing or drawing. Then the player could consult a listing of card combinations in order to see whether to draw or stand. This refinement, in all its precise detail, is

* See footnote p. 15.

impractical for two reasons. It is difficult, perhaps at present impossible, to calculate and its bulk (many thousands of entries) would prevent the player from memorizing and using it in play. Furthermore, the net gain is quite small.

However, the running count in conjunction with the Tens strategy does take into account the cards the player draws. It is not as precise as the strategy outlined in the foregoing because it only classifies cards into two crude categories, Tens and others. But it does gain much, even most, of the difference.

TABLE 1. *Dealer's Probabilities.*

Dealer shows	Dealer's total 17	18	19	20	21	natural	busts
2	1390	1318	1318	1239	1205	...	3530
3	1303	1309	1238	1233	1160	...	3756
4	1310	1142	1207	1163	1151	...	4028
5	1197	1235	1169	1047	1063	...	4289
6	1670	1065	1072	1007	0979	...	4208
7	3723	1386	0773	0789	0730	...	2599
8	1309	3630	1294	0683	0698	...	2386
9	1219	1039	3574	1223	0611	...	2334
10	1144	1129	1147	3289	0365	0784	2143
A	1261	1310	1295	1316	0516	3137	1165
overall probability	1458	1381	1348	1758	0736	0483	2836

Table 1 gives the probability that the dealer will achieve a specified total, for each possible value of his up card. The rows of the table do not generally quite add up to one because of small round-off and approximation errors. The defect is no more than 10^{-4} and so for practical purposes is negligible. The column totals show slight discrepancies with the over-all probability figures because the original table had five figures and was rounded off *after* the columns were summed.

From this point on, all tables (except Table 5) are computed on the assumption the dealer does not have a natural.

TABLE 2a. *Player's Gain by Drawing, Over Standing, with Hard Totals.*

Dealer	Player's hard total								
shows	**12**	**13**	**14**	**15**	**16**	**17**	**18**	**19**	**20**
2	039	−016	−071	−130	−190	−401	−764	−1.140	−1.487
3	015	−044	−106	−170	−233	−438	−793	−1.121	−1.497
4	−013	−080	−148	−215	−283	−492	−793	−1.139	−1.506
5	−040	−112	−184	−256	−327	−487	−826	−1.181	−1.534
6	−023	−093	−163	−233	−262	−508	−882	−1.213	−1.554
7	209	165	121	118	078	−365	−986	−1.329	−1.624
8	188	148	149	111	074	−105	−685	−1.302	−1.641
9	141	143	106	070	033	−135	−425	−986	−1.603
10	154	118	081	045	008	−162	−474	−806	−1.410
A	253	226	200	173	143	−089	−542	−1.029	−1.545

To illustrate the use of Table 2a, suppose you have a hard total of twelve and the dealer shows a Two. If you decide to draw, rather than stand, your gain is 0.039. This means that, on the average over a large number of situations like this one, if you always draw to hard 12 against a 2, rather than stand, you will be better off by approximately an additional 3.9 per cent of your initial bet. If an entry is positive in the table, the player should draw, rather than stand. Conversely, if an entry is negative the player should stand, not draw. The inspection of this table immediately yields the hard standing numbers. This is, in fact, how they were first obtained.

Similar remarks apply to Table 2b except that the entries yield the soft standing numbers.

There are two extremely close decisions, one in each of Tables 2a and 2b. In Table 2a, the player who stands rather than draws on hard sixteen against a ten loses, in these situations, an average amount of about 0.8 per cent of his wager.

TABLE 2b. *Player's Gain by Drawing, Over Standing, with Soft Totals.*

Dealer shows	Player's soft total 17	18	19	20
2	142	– 074	– 285	– 461
3	132	– 076	– 253	– 445
4	115	– 054	– 238	– 422
5	138	– 052	– 239	– 412
6	119	– 093	– 260	– 422
7	158	– 235	– 403	– 529
8	315	– 068	– 450	– 611
9	264	083	– 284	– 660
10	225	029	– 175	– 557
A	292	– 007	– 312	– 611

In Table 2b, the player who draws rather than stands on soft eighteen against an Ace loses about 0.7 per cent in such situations. Some players I know of attempted to solve blackjack empirically; that is, they dealt out many hundreds, or even thousands, of hands and recorded results, in an effort to decide which standing numbers were correct for various up cards of the dealer. As might be expected, these players were sharply divided over these two close decisions.

Table 3 was computed directly from Table 1 as follows. Suppose the player to hold a given total, say 19, when the dealer's up card is a *6*. The player's advantage is then the sum of the probabilities that the dealer will receive a poorer total (18,17 or busts), $0.1065 + 0.1670 + 0.4208 = 0.6943$, minus the probability the dealer will have a better total (20 or 21), $0.1007 + 0.0979 = 0.1986$. The difference $0.6943 - 0.1986$ equals 0.4957 and rounding off to three significant figures we get 0.496, in agreement with the appropriate entry of Table 3.

We are assuming in Table 3, as was remarked earlier, that the dealer does not have a natural. In this situation the player holding a natural always wins 1.5 times his original

TABLE 3. *Player's Advantage Standing on Various Totals.*

Dealer shows	Player's total 16	17	18	19	20	21
2	– 294	– 155	116	379	635	879
3	– 249	– 119	143	397	644	884
4	– 194	– 063	182	417	653	885
5	– 142	– 023	221	461	683	894
6	– 159	009	282	496	704	902
7	– 480	– 108	403	619	775	927
8	– 523	– 392	102	594	792	930
9	– 533	– 411	– 185	276	756	939
10	– 535	– 411	– 164	083	564	960
A	– 660	– 477	– 102	278	658	925

bet; that is, his advantage, in the sense that we are using the term, is 150 per cent. Thus there is no need to list that alternative in the table.

Table 4 gives the player's advantage for all possible pairs of hole cards against a given up card of the dealer, assuming first that the player simply stands or draws using the proper standing numbers (deduced from Tables 2a and 2b). Then the player's advantage, assuming that he doubles down, is given. Finally, the player's advantage is given for the cases in which his hole cards are numerically equal and he splits the pair and then does the most advantageous of the two alternatives of doubling down or drawing and standing. The table is divided into ten main sections, one for each value of the dealer's up card.

The basic strategy for each value of the dealer's up card can be deduced from the table as follows. First, suppose the hole cards form a pair. Compare the player's advantage from splitting the pair with his advantage from doubling down and from drawing. If it is greater than these, he should split. Otherwise he should do the more advantageous of doubling down and splitting. For example, on holding (*4,4*) against a Ten, splitting gives an advantage of —0.542; doubling down gives an advantage of —0.722; and drawing and standing, using a hard standing number of seventeen and a soft standing number of eighteen, gives an advantage of −0.239. Because this latter figure is the smallest of the three, then drawing and standing is the best of the alternatives. Thus the player should not double down or split in this instance.

If the player's hole cards are (*A*,*2*), this is the same as (*2*,*A*), so only one of these two spots is filled in the table. Thus the subsections of Table 4 get their peculiar triangular shape.

Table 4 sheds further light on points about the basic strategy. For example, in the footnote to Table 3.5, it is asserted that the player should not double down but instead should draw on (*9*,*2*) versus an Ace but that the difference is nil. Table 4 shows us that the difference is, in fact, 0.153 − 0.150, or 0.3 per cent. In the discussion of pair splitting for the basic strategy (pages 29-30), we say that if a pair of Aces is not split, the hand is "only fair for doubling down or drawing or standing," whereas splitting gives us a good chance for a winning hand. Table 4 gives us the precise advantage for the most profitable of the two alternatives of doubling down or standing and drawing. We see that the numbers waver around 0, with some positive and some negative. However the corresponding advantage for *splitting* the Aces is generally considerably positive, as shown by the table. Similarly, the rough oversimplification in Chapter 3, that the splitting of a pair of eights against *7* through *A* breaks up a bad hand and replaces it by two average hands, is (only roughly) borne out by the table.

For the complete deck, Table 4 was used to compute the player's average advantage against various up cards of the dealer's and then the player's over-all advantage was found. Similar results were obtained for the other decks from the appropriate data. The results are listed in Table 5. They give some evidence of how much the various figures we give are affected when the composition of the deck, or the rules, vary.

TABLE 4a. *Dealer's Up Card Is Ten*

	Player's hole cards → ↓	A	2	3	4	5	6	7	8	9	10
Drawing and standing	**A**	—044									
	2	—084	—267								
	3	—119	—301	—337							
	4	—167	—341	—330	—239						
	5	—225	—318	—249	—143	035					
	6	—184	—242	—138	038	121	—380				
	7	—131	—146	039	120	—379	—442	—504			
	8	083	036	118	—381	—444	—460	—468	—508		
	9	564	112	—385	—397	—453	—508	—508	—411	—164	
	10	...	—345	—392	—446	—503	—508	—411	—164	083	564
Doubling down	**A**	—465									
	2	—465	—1.070								
	3	—470	—1.070	—1.050							
	4	—490	—1.050	—933	—722						
	5	—531	—933	—722	—432	029					
	6	—424	—722	—432	029	202	—780				
	7	—324	—432	024	192	—780	—895	—1.023			
	8	—237	014	181	—794	—902	—927	—939	—1.015		
	9	—058	162	—811	—811	—908	—1.019	—1.015	—1.111	—1.248	
	10	...	—730	—806	—897	—1.003	—1.015	—1.111	—1.248	—1.425	—1.680
Pair splitting		207	—434	—480	—542	—633	—625	—594	—446	—279	018

TABLE 4b. *Dealer's Up Card Is Nine*

	Player's hole cards → ↓	A	2	3	4	5	6	7	8	9	10
Drawing and standing	A	—021									
	2	—027	—228								
	3	—067	—262	—305							
	4	—121	—306	—301	—206						
	5	—175	—288	—217	—050	124					
	6	—143	—211	—045	126	156	—382				
	7	—099	—053	128	155	—386	—415	—471			
	8	276	127	150	—387	—408	—431	—437	—480		
	9	756	144	—387	—362	—424	—477	—480	—411	—185	
	10	. . .	—347	—358	—414	—476	—480	—411	—185	276	756
Doubling down	A	—467									
	2	—407	—1.066								
	3	—412	—1.066	—1.046							
	4	—440	—1.046	—930	—692						
	5	—472	—930	—692	—265	191					
	6	—361	—692	—265	191	257	—800				
	7	—274	—265	186	247	—810	—854	—965			
	8	—082	177	229	—824	—843	—879	—883	—959		
	9	098	209	—832	—755	—859	—962	—959	—1.056	—1.189	
	10	. . .	—753	—750	—840	—955	—959	—1.056	—1.189	—1.397	—1.683
Pair splitting		262	—378	—384	—450	—555	—533	—522	—371	—085	183

TABLE 4c. *Dealer's Up Card Is Eight*

	Player's hole cards → ↓	A	2	3	4	5	6	7	8	9	10
Drawing and standing	A	079									
	2	028	—148								
	3	022	—189	—241							
	4	—043	—238	—236	—054						
	5	—093	—224	—064	110	207					
	6	—076	—060	114	209	229	—322				
	7	102	107	212	223	—322	—394	—409			
	8	594	206	217	—318	—387	—370	—380	—426		
	9	792	218	—317	—336	—369	—419	—426	—392	102	
	10	. . .	—277	—332	—358	—419	—426	—392	102	594	792
Doubling down	A	—342									
	2	—347	—1.046								
	3	—293	—1.046	—1.024							
	4	—333	—1.024	—858	—434						
	5	—353	—858	—434	017	331					
	6	—249	—434	017	331	373	—704				
	7	—027	017	325	353	—704	—836	—855			
	8	195	305	333	—707	—822	—770	—775	—853		
	9	226	325	—713	—723	—762	—854	—853	—952	—1.132	
	10	. . .	—634	—717	—742	—848	—853	—952	—1.132	—1.392	—1.685
Pair splitting		378	—197	—252	—287	—391	—371	—377	—051	226	354

TABLE 4d. *Dealer's Up Card Is Seven*

	Player's hole cards → ↓	A	2	3	4	5	6	7	8	9	10
Drawing and standing	**A**	152									
	2	100	—099								
	3	050	—129	—177							
	4	020	—176	—088	092						
	5	—033	—076	083	187	270					
	6	052	089	189	274	291	—269				
	7	403	182	272	285	—263	—334	—392			
	8	619	265	285	—254	—333	—353	—328	—378		
	9	775	286	—253	—282	—353	—367	—378	—108	403	
	10	. . .	—213	—274	—348	—367	—378	—108	403	619	775
Doubling down	**A**	—186									
	2	—193	—961								
	3	—214	—961	—900							
	4	—186	—900	—573	—144						
	5	—214	—573	—144	167	485					
	6	005	—144	167	458	497	—598				
	7	246	167	443	476	—586	—713	—823			
	8	331	422	467	—577	—701	—738	—672	—757		
	9	356	461	—583	—611	—732	—750	—757	—902	—1.131	
	10	. . .	—504	—596	—723	—744	—757	—902	—1.131	—1.396	—1.685
Pair splitting		512	—012	—087	—184	—239	—218	—054	267	370	490

TABLE 4e. *Dealer's Up Card Is Six*

Player's hole cards → ↓		A	2	3	4	5	6	7	8	9	10
Drawing and standing	A	179									
	2	149	008								
	3	122	—009	—017							
	4	089	—017	024	135						
	5	084	037	124	218	313					
	6	133	125	218	313	354	—158				
	7	282	207	309	349	—158	—158	—158			
	8	496	304	344	—158	—158	—158	—158	—158		
	9	704	340	—158	—158	—158	—158	—158	009	282	
	10	. . .	—158	—158	—158	—158	—158	009	282	496	704
Doubling down	A	158									
	2	176	—317								
	3	161	—317	—289							
	4	133	—289	—136	105						
	5	153	—136	105	350	625					
	6	267	105	350	625	709	—401				
	7	392	350	618	698	—398	—573	—743			
	8	481	607	689	—400	—572	—657	—733	—793		
	9	555	680	—408	—483	—649	—811	—793	—958	—1.167	
	10	. . .	—330	—476	—640	—803	—793	—958	—1.167	—1.411	—1.689
Pair splitting		716	210	175	126	065	151	232	368	451	555

TABLE 4f. *Dealer's Up Card Is Five*

	Player's hole cards → ↓	A	2	3	4	5	6	7	8	9	10
Drawing and standing	A	174									
	2	148	013								
	3	122	—005	—022							
	4	091	—022	013	113						
	5	062	025	103	203	300					
	6	120	104	202	300	350	—142				
	7	221	192	298	345	—142	—142	—142			
	8	461	293	340	—142	—142	—142	—142	—142		
	9	683	335	—142	—142	—142	—142	—142	—023	221	
	10	. . .	—142	—142	—142	—142	—142	—023	221	461	683
Doubling down	A	192									
	2	182	—284								
	3	167	—284	—265							
	4	138	—265	—147	071						
	5	107	—147	071	323	601					
	6	240	071	323	601	699	—398				
	7	350	323	596	689	—398	—577	—753			
	8	454	586	679	—402	—575	—667	—747	—896		
	9	534	670	—411	—488	—658	—825	—896	—978	—1.178	
	10	. . .	—333	—483	—648	—816	—896	—978	—1.178	—1.416	—1.691
Pair splitting		704	211	184	141	067	119	206	324	426	533

TABLE 4g. *Dealer's Up Card Is Four*

Player's hole cards → ↓		A	2	3	4	5	6	7	8	9	10
Drawing and standing	**A**	132									
	2	107	—033								
	3	082	—051	—071							
	4	050	—071	—043	070						
	5	019	—030	059	158	262					
	6	057	058	158	262	316	—194				
	7	182	147	259	311	—194	—194	—194			
	8	417	254	306	—194	—194	—194	—194	—194		
	9	653	301	—194	—194	—194	—194	—194	—063	182	
	10	. . .	—194	—194	—194	—194	—194	—063	182	417	653
Doubling down	**A**	108									
	2	103	—389								
	3	088	—389	—367							
	4	058	—367	—242	—022						
	5	024	—242	—022	231	524					
	6	113	—022	231	524	632	—448				
	7	268	231	518	622	—448	—614	—784			
	8	368	508	612	—452	—614	—698	—772	—913		
	9	455	602	—462	—527	—688	—848	—913	—1.075	—1.191	
	10	. . .	—385	—522	—679	—839	—913	—1.075	—1.191	—1.422	—1.692
Pair splitting		637	095	068	028	—039	005	058	224	331	454

TABLE 4h. *Dealer's Up Card Is Three*

Player's hole cards → ↓		A	2	3	4	5	6	7	8	9	10
Drawing and standing	A	106									
	2	069	—078								
	3	046	—095	—117							
	4	014	—116	—089	017						
	5	—018	—077	006	123	232					
	6	018	007	123	231	287	—249				
	7	143	111	228	281	—249	—249	—249			
	8	397	223	276	—252	—249	—249	—249	—249		
	9	644	270	—257	—249	—249	—249	—249	—119	143	
	10	. . .	—218	—249	—249	—249	—249	—119	143	397	644
Doubling down	A	024									
	2	024	—498								
	3	013	—498	—476							
	4	—019	—476	—349	—115						
	5	—054	—349	—115	155	461					
	6	035	—115	155	461	573	—499				
	7	143	155	456	563	—498	—652	—810			
	8	299	445	522	—503	—652	—723	—789	—922		
	9	389	524	—513	—564	—713	—866	—922	—1.076	—1.273	
	10	. . .	—436	—559	—703	—856	—922	—1.076	—1.273	—1.424	—1.692
Pair splitting		579	007	—041	—078	143	110	—064	096	252	393

TABLE 4i. *Dealer's Up Card Is Two*

Player's hole cards → ↓		A	2	3	4	5	6	7	8	9	10
Drawing and standing	A	084									
	2	040	—113								
	3	016	—130	—151							
	4	—015	—151	—123	—014						
	5	—047	—110	—024	085	207					
	6	—008	—024	083	207	264	—270				
	7	116	072	204	259	—270	—294	—294			
	8	379	197	253	—272	—294	—294	—294	—294		
	9	335	247	—277	—294	—294	—294	—294	—155	116	
	10	. . .	—239	—294	—294	—294	—294	—155	116	379	635
Doubling down	A	—045									
	2	—045	—588								
	3	—051	—588	—566							
	4	—079	—566	—431	—188						
	5	—116	—431	—188	093	410					
	6	—022	—188	093	410	524	—540				
	7	090	093	404	513	—540	—687	—833			
	8	193	393	502	—544	—686	—746	—800	—927		
	9	334	491	—554	—599	—736	—877	—927	—1.075	—1.270	
	10	. . .	—478	—593	—725	—867	—927	—1.075	—1.268	—1.503	—1.693
Pair splitting		529	062	—124	—161	—223	—195	—134	030	158	341

TABLE 4j. *Dealer's Up Card Is One*

Player's hole cards →	↓	A	2	3	4	5	6	7	8	9	10
Drawing and standing	A	—015									
	2	—056	—251								
	3	—091	—285	—328							
	4	—146	—329	—339	—208						
	5	—200	—327	—218	—077	075					
	6	—185	—211	—072	077	165	—371				
	7	—102	—081	079	161	—371	—435	—492			
	8	277	075	157	—371	—433	—450	—457	—498		
	9	658	153	—373	—385	—445	—496	—498	—477	—102	
	10	. . .	—334	—381	—436	—493	—498	—477	—102	277	658
Doubling down	A	—573									
	2	—573	—1.321								
	3	—580	—1.321	—1.299							
	4	—611	—1.299	—1.133	—811						
	5	—652	—1.133	—811	—426	008					
	6	—528	—811	—426	008	196	—840				
	7	—376	—426	001	181	—840	—942	—1.035			
	8	—228	—014	166	—848	—937	—945	—933	—996		
	9	—095	150	—589	—843	—930	—1.011	—996	—1.097	—1.259	
	10	. . .	—781	—836	—914	—1.001	—996	—1.097	—1.259	—1.483	—1.764
Pair splitting		204	—410	—457	—523	—614	—605	—622	—391	—158	090

TABLE 5. *Player's Advantage Against Various Up Cards.*

Description of deck	Player's overall advantage*	Player's advantage when the dealer's up card is 1*	2	3	4	5	6	7	8	9	10*
one deck	—0021	—364	094	130	176	229	236	145	056	—040	—173
one deck, soft 17	—0034	—393	095	130	177	230	239	145	056	—040	—173
two decks	—0038	—351	092	146	167	212	235	144	057	—041	—173
Q(*1*) = 0.	—0272	...	031	065	112	157	203	061	—021	—104	—208
Q(2) = 0.	0142	—373	...	149	194	289	308	184	105	008	—174
Q(*3*) = 0.	0189	—371	120	...	233	312	339	200	111	—030	—171
Q(*4*) = 0.	0236	—374	126	195	...	358	378	220	076	—022	—169
Q(*5*) = 0.	0329	—369	184	240	315	...	409	186	081	—012	—160
Q(*6*) = 0.	0187	—385	179	240	313	370	...	165	068	—040	—172
Q(*7*) = 0.	0125	—364	171	236	289	233	232	...	086	—023	—178
Q(*8*) = 0.	0005	—356	159	206	148	196	215	141	...	—038	—166
Q(*9*) = 0.	—0091	—343	131	067	124	181	176	142	031	...	—154
Q(*10*) = 12.	—0215	—346	024	050	089	137	154	117	038	—046	—160
Q(*10*) = 20.	0189	—385	176	212	259	310	314	171	073	—030	—176
Q(*10*) = 24.	0394	—404	249	284	337	391	390	194	092	—014	—173
Q(*1*) = 0. and Q(*10*) = 24.	0070	...	186	219	264	307	362	115	016	—072	—215

* The possibility of the dealer having a natural has been included in these figures.

Some Common Blackjack Errors

The basic strategy for blackjack was first published (with a few insignificant* errors) by Baldwin *et al.* [2] four years before this book was begun. In spite of that fact, blackjack strategies containing gross errors continue to appear.† In the discussion to follow, we will consider some of these errors. We will formulate several experiments, some of which will take the reader less than an hour. Each experiment compares a feature of the basic strategy with one of the commonly made gross errors.

These experiments should convince almost anyone who tries them that the basic strategy is correct on these points and that the other strategies are in serious error. Study of these experiments should enable you to formulate your own experiments for testing the gross points of difference between the basic strategy and any other strategy. We can, in principle, test *any* discrepancy, not merely the large ones; however, in the case of close decisions, the experiments are unpleasantly long.

First Experiment: Drawing Versus Standing Holding Hard 16 Against an Ace

Table 2a shows us that the player who draws rather than stands on hard sixteen when the dealer has an Ace showing gains 14.3 per cent, on the average, in such situations. Put another way, to stand rather than draw on hard sixteen *costs* the player on the average 14.3 per cent. The follow-

* We call them insignificant because they cost the player on the average a mere 0.04 per cent of his action.

† In this section we are comparing the basic strategy only with other strategies in which complete deck composition is assumed, that is, strategies which do not count cards.

ing experiment is designed to verify this. Remove an Ace from a complete deck and place it face up on the table. This represents the dealer's up card. Next, write the number 16 on a card or paper and place it in front of yourself. This represents your hard total.

Of course, this does not correspond exactly to the real situation. In a game the cards that the player actually has drawn to make up his total of hard 16 will alter the advantage in drawing. Conceivably, if enough small cards are used to comprise the total, it may even be wise to stand. For example, in the very close decision as to whether to stand or draw when holding hard 16 and the dealer's up card is a Ten, drawing is favored over standing with an average gain of 0.8 per cent according to Table 2a. However, when the player's hard 16 total is composed of (*4,4,4,4*), we have a precise figure (that is, involving none of the approximations that were necessary to make most of the calculations in the book) for the player's *disadvantage* in drawing. According to other computer results, not given in this appendix, the edge is 6.267 per cent in favor of standing.

The objection to the use of a paper total in our experiment is answered as follows. A player could replace our experiment by one in which a real game of blackjack was played and in which the player kept a record of the results of standing versus drawing in the hard 16 versus a Ten situation. Our assertion is that the average long-run result would be within a few tenths of a per cent of the 14.3 per cent figure based on paper totals, as argued in an earlier footnote in this appendix, so much time and trouble can be saved by a paper total experiment. The same considerations apply to the other experiments we suggest.

To return to our experiment, now shuffle the deck and deal two hundred dealer "hands" as follows. Assume you stand on 16 and deal a card to the dealer (his hole card). If he gets a natural, discard the Ten-value card and do not record the result. We do this because the question of whether or not to draw on hard 16 arises only if the dealer has already checked and found he has no natural. If the hole card is not a *10,* continue dealing until the dealer either busts or achieves a total, soft or hard, of 17 or more. If the dealer busts, you win. If he does not bust, you lose. Record the result. Discard the used cards and deal another hand. When one hundred "hands" are dealt in this fashion the player will win, on an average, about 17 of the hands and lose the rest. This follows from the assertion of Table 3, that the player who stands on 16 when the dealer shows an Ace *loses* at the rate of 66 per cent.

Next, deal two hundred hands as follows. Give the dealer one card (his hole card). If it is a Ten, discard it and deal another card for the same reasons as before. Now assume you draw exactly one card to a total of 16. If you bust, you lose. Discard the card and record the loss. If you do not bust you have a hard total between 17 and 21. Stop drawing to your own hand and, if necessary, proceed to give the dealer further cards until he either busts or gets a total of 17 or more. Record whether you won, tied, or lost, and continue.

Your percentage of "wins" should be figured as the number of wins plus one-half of the ties (to tie every hand, for example, would be substantially the same as winning half and losing half, for no net gain). In this part of the experiment, the average number of "wins" per hundred hands should be 24.15. Thus, with two hundred hands the average separation between the two ways of playing hard 16 against an Ace will be $2 \times (24.15 - 17.00)$ or 14.3 hands. There will be, however, chance deviations in each part of the experiment from the cited average totals. In fact, once in 50 times, standing on 16 against an Ace will produce better results, over 200 hands, than drawing.

The suggestion that the player should draw, rather than

stand, holding 13 against a *1* can be tested in the same way only here a decisive experiment is considerably longer because the difference in net gain (loss) between the two strategies is smaller, only 4.4 per cent. We suggest 1000 or more hands of each type.

Second Experiment: Doubling Down on Hard Ten Versus an Ace

This is conducted in much the same way as the previous experiment. Select as hole cards (*8,2*) for the maximum error of 8.9 per cent, in order to shorten the experiment. This figure of 8.9 per cent is obtained from Table 4j where we see that, holding (*8,2*) versus an Ace, if we simply draw until we reach a suitable total, we win about 7.5 per cent of our bet, in the long run. However if we double down we lose 1.4 per cent of our original bet in the long run. The net difference is 7.5 — (−1.4) or 8.9 per cent. Play about 400 hands in which you double down. Afterwards, subtract the number of hands lost from the number of hands won. Then double this number (to take into account your doubled bet on the double down hands) to get your total profit in the 400 hands by doubling down against the Ace. Remember as before to disregard all dealer naturals in your tally by giving the dealer another hole card if he has a Ten under.

Next, play 400 hands in which you follow the correct drawing and standing strategy versus an Ace (Table 3.8). Your wins minus your losses give your profit for the 400 hands. On the average in 400 hands, you will have an excess of wins over losses of about 15.0 hands with drawing and standing. With doubling down, you will have an average excess of *losses over wins* of 1.40 hands, or an average loss of 2.80 units.

Third Experiment: Splitting a Pair of Sixes Against a Five

According to Table 4f, the gain here by splitting, rather than standing, is 11.9 + 14.2 or 26.1 per cent. If you stand, you will win about 42.9 hands out of each hundred for a net loss of 14.2 units per hundred bets. If you split, your hundred hands become 200 and you will win about 11.9 more of those 200 hands than you lose. You have an average net gain of 26.1 units per hundred original hands by splitting rather than standing. Only fifty original hands of each type should be decisive.

Mimicking the Dealer

To quote Baldwin *et al.* [2, p. 439], "The player who mimics the dealer, drawing to 16 or less, standing on 17 or more, never doubling down or splitting pairs, has an expectation of −0.056." That is, the dealer has a 5.6 per cent edge.

Let us illustrate the use of Table 1 by computing a figure for the player who mimics the dealer. First notice that when the player follows these rules, the game is symmetric except for two situations. If both the dealer and player bust (count the dealer as a bust if he would have busted supposing that, although the player busts and bets are settled, the dealer plays out his hand anyway), the dealer wins. This favors the dealer and the edge it gives him is the probability that both dealer and player bust. Since the dealer and player are assumed to be using the same strategies, Table 1, the table of dealer's probabilities, applies to both of them. The over-all probability of each busting is therefore 0.2836 and (assuming stochastic independence, not strictly valid but good in this instance to a high degree of approximation when the deck is nearly complete) the probability of both busting is (0.2836×0.2836), or 8.04 per cent, in favor of the dealer, as a result of this factor. The second nonsymmetry in the game is the fact that the player wins 1.5 units when he has a natural and the dealer does not. The dealer, on the other hand, only wins one unit from the player when he has a natural and the player does not. This happens 4.68 per cent of the time for each side, so the player gains one-half that amount, or 2.34 per cent from this factor. Thus, the net dealer's edge is (8.07 – 2.34), or 5.73 per cent. [If we recall the footnote at the beginning of Chapter 3, we see that (5.73 – 0.37) per cent, or 5.36 per cent, is a better figure.]

The Player Who Never Busts

Another interesting figure to calculate is the advantage which the casino has against a player who never draws to a possible bust hand. First we note that this means the player's hard standing numbers are all twelve. However, the soft standing numbers are not determined. Thus the problem is meaningless as stated. Since it is unanswerable as it stands, we assume soft standing numbers of 17 and proceed. As we pointed out earlier, common sense dictates that the soft standing number should always be at least 17. We know that 18 is always better than 17 so 17 gives the player a greater average rate of loss than he would have with soft standing numbers of 18. We will call a player using this curious strategy "conservative."

We assert the true figure for the house advantage against a conservative player is between 5 and 8 per cent. Our evidence comes from three sources. First, we ran an experiment in which six groups of 100 hands each were played with the conservative strategy. The number of player units lost ranged from 13 to 2, with an average of 7. The agreement with our figure of 5 to 8 per cent is good. Since the figure of six hundred hands was selected in advance and not influenced by the results of the early hands, we can apply the usual formulas to conclude that with probability 98 per cent, the true figure for the house advantage lies between 3 and 11 per cent. Second we ran a hand calculation (which is comparatively easy because of the low hard standing numbers) that proved that the true figure was well below 10 per cent. Third and best, Baldwin and his co-authors give a figure of 4.25 per cent for the house advantage against a player who stands on hard twelve, never doubles down, and splits Aces and Eights only. (They fail to specify the soft standing numbers.) It can be shown that splitting Aces and Eights adds less than 1 per cent to the player's advantage. The correction, if any, for different soft standing numbers is also, overall, of the order of 1 or 2 per cent. Thus the true figure estimated from this source is between 5 or 6 per cent and 8 per cent.

References

[1] ASHBAUGH, DON, "Game for Gaming," *Las Vegas Review Journal* (Sunday Feature Section), December 25, 1960, pp. 20, 22.

[2] BALDWIN, ROGER; CANTEY, WILBERT; MAISEL, HERBERT; and McDERMOTT, JAMES, "The Optimum Strategy in Blackjack," *Journal of the American Statistical Association*, Vol. 51, 429-439 (1956).

[3] ———. *Playing Blackjack to Win; A New Strategy for the Game of 21* (M. Barrows & Co., Inc., New York, 1957).

[4] *Boston Globe*, January 24, 1961, pp. 1, 11.

[5] CARDANO, GEROLAMO, *Book on Games of Chance* (first published about 1620). Translated by SIDNEY H. GOULD (Holt, Rhinehart and Winston, Inc., New York, and San Francisco, 1961).

[6] *Columbus Dispatch*, January 30, 1961, p. 1-B.

[7] CRAWFORD, JOHN R., *How to Be a Consistent Winner in the Most Popular Card Games* (Doubleday and Co., Inc., New York, 1953).

[8] CULBERTSON, ELY; MOREHEAD, ALBERT; MOTT-SMITH, GEOFFREY, *Culbertson's Card Games Complete, with Official Rules* (The Greystone Press, New York, 1952).

[9] FELLER, WILLIAM, *An Introduction to Probability Theory and Its Applications,* Vol. I (John Wiley & Sons, Inc., New York, 1957).

[10] FOX, PHILLIP G. (as told to STANLEY FOX), "A Primer for Chumps," *Saturday Evening Post,* November 21, 1959, pp. 31ff.

[11] FREY, RICHARD L., *According to Hoyle* (Fawcett Publications, Inc., Greenwich, Conn., 1956).

[12] FURST, DR. BRUNO, *The Practical Way to a Better Memory* (Fawcett Publications, Inc., Greenwich, Conn., 1957).

[13] GARCIA, FRANK, *Marked Cards and Loaded Dice* (Prentice-Hall, Inc., New York, 1962).

[14] HUFF, DARRELL, *The Mathematics of Sex, Gambling and Insurance* (Harper & Brothers, New York, 1959).

[15] JONES, JACK, *Golden Nugget Gaming Guide* (Silver State Publishing Co., Las Vegas, 1949).

[16] KATCHER, LEO, *The Big Bankroll; the Life and Times of Arnold Rothstein* (Harper & Brothers, New York, 1959).

[17] K. C. Card Co., *Forty-second Anniversary Blue Book, 1960,* Chicago, 1959.

[18] KELLY, J. L., "A New Interpretation of Information Rate," *IRE Transactions on Information Theory,* Vol. IT-2, No. 3, September, 1956. *Bell System Tech. J.,* Vol. 35, 917-926 (1956).

[19] *Las Vegas Sun,* January 25 and 27, 1961.

[20] LEWIS, OSCAR, *Sagebrush Casinos: The Story of Legal Gambling in Nevada* (Doubleday & Co., Inc., New York, 1953).

[21] *Life,* "Senators Survey Low-Belly Strippers," September 1, 1961, p. 39.

[22] MACDOUGALL, MICHAEL, *MacDougall on Dice and Cards* (Coward-McCann, Inc., New York, 1944).

[23] MCKINSEY, JOHN C., *Introduction to the Theory of Games* (McGraw-Hill Book Co., Inc., New York, 1952).

[24] *Miami News,* January 25, 1961, p. 6A.

[25] *The Nation,* February 4, 1961.

[26] *Newsweek,* "Gambling: Hello Suckers," September 4, 1961, pp. 22ff.

[27] *New York Herald Tribune,* January 29, 1961, pp. 1, 24.

[28] ROBB, INEZ, "Bets Are Off," *New York World-Telegram and Sun,* February 7, 1961.

[29] ORE, ØYSTEIN, *Cardano, The Gambling Scholar* [with a translation (from the Latin of Cardano's book, *Games of Chance*) by SIDNEY HENRY GOULD] (Princeton University Press, Princeton, N. J., 1953).

[30] POINCARÉ, HENRI, *Science and Method.* Translated by Francis Maitland (Dover Publications, Inc., New York, 1958).

[31] RADNER, SIDNEY H., *How to Spot Card Sharps and Their Methods* (Key Publishing Co., New York, 1957).

[32] The RAND Corporation, *A Million Random Digits with 100,000 Normal Deviates* (Free Press of Glencoe, Illinois, 1955).

[33] *Reno Evening Gazette,* January 26, 1961.

[34] SCARNE, JOHN, *Scarne's Complete Guide to Gambling* (Simon and Shuster, Inc., New York, 1961).

[35] *Scientific American,* "How to Beat the Game," April, 1961, p. 84.

[36] Showboat Hotel, Las Vegas, Nevada, "The Univac '21' Formula for Standing or Drawing."

[37] *Sports Illustrated,* "Calculated Risk," February 6, 1961, pp. 4, 5.

[38] STEEN, JOAN, "Exposing Crooked Gambler's Tricks," *Popular Science Monthly,* January, 1962, pp. 61ff.

[39] THORP, EDWARD O., "Fortune's Formula: The Game of Blackjack," *Notices of the American Mathematical Society,* December, 1960, pp. 935-936.

[40] ———. "A Favorable Strategy for Twenty-One," *Proceedings of the National Academy of Sciences,* Vol. 47, No. 1, 110-112 (1961).

[41] ———. "A Prof Beats the Gamblers," *The Atlantic Monthly,* June, 1962.

[42] *Times,* Modern Living: "Eight Days to Win," January 13, 1961, p. 82ff.

[43] *Washington Post and Times Herald,* January 25, 1961, p. 3; editorial, "High Stakes," p. A16, January 26, 1961.

[44] WILLIAMS, JOHN D., The Compleat Strategyst (McGraw-Hill Book Co., Inc., New York, 1954).

Index*

* fn denotes that the particular item may be found in a footnote on the given page.

A NOTE ABOUT THE AUTHOR

EDWARD O. THORP is currently teaching at New Mexico State University where he is an Assistant Professor of Mathematics. Prior to this post, from 1959-1961, Professor Thorp was a C.L.E. Moore instructor at the Massachusetts Institute of Technology. He has also taught at the University of California at Los Angeles, from which he received a Ph.D. in 1958. Professor Thorp is a member of the American Mathematical Society and the Edinburgh Mathematical Society. One of his major fields of interest is probability theory.

A NOTE ON THE PRODUCTION

The text of this book was set on the Linotype in a face called TIMES ROMAN, designed by Stanley Morison for *The Times* of London, and first introduced by that newspaper in 1932.

Shortly thereafter, TIMES ROMAN was made available throughout the English-speaking world, and it became one of the most popular modern book faces. Morison's intent in designing this type face is perhaps best expressed in a few sentences that he wrote in 1930: "Type design moves at the pace of the most conservative reader. The good type designer therefore realizes that, for a new format to be successful, it has to be so good that only very few recognize its novelty. If readers do not notice the consummate reticence and rare discipline of a new type, it is probably a good letter." Most students of typography agree that in the creation of TIMES ROMAN, Morison has successfully met this criterion.

This book was composed, printed, and bound by the H. WOLFF BOOK MANUFACTURING COMPANY of New York City. The paper was manufactured by the OXFORD PAPER COMPANY, also of New York City. GUY FLEMING of Sagaponack, New York designed the book.